Hello, girls!
Every year you send me a lovely selection of colour photographs which I can't use in the weekly issues of "Judy". But this year I have saved them up and we have printed them here and at the back of the book. *Beatrice*

I took the photograph of my fellow passengers boarding our 'plane at Prestwick Airport at the start of my holiday. We were going to Spain.
Rhoda McEwan,
Stirling.

I photographed the new Post Office Tower when visiting London. It always reminds me of an enormous lollipop.
Joan Gregory,
Middlesbrough.

My pet rabbit's name is Tanya and she loves to bask in the sun on our front doorstep. My family are accustomed to seeing her there, but unexpected callers to the house often get a shock.
Ruth Watson,
Newcastle.

My
mother
ok this picture of me
laxing on the beach at
lo Di Jesolo in Italy.
e weather was
rvellous.
ia Hill,
on.

The river winding into the distance is the River Tay, in Scotland. I snapped this view when I was on holiday at Perth last summer.
Mary Boland,
Dublin.

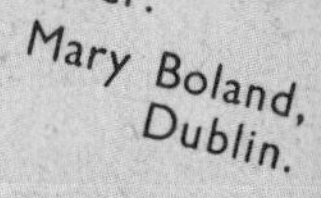

Judy BOOK *for* GIRLS

Printed by D. C. Thomson & Co., Ltd., Dundee,
and Buckley & Bland Ltd., Stockport.
Published by D. C. Thomson & Co., Ltd., Dundee.

Fay Farrell

FISHERMEN'S NURSE

FAY FARRELL is nursing in the Scottish fishing village of Starnoch Head. One morning she receives a telephone call from John Gordon, who says his wife is acting strangely.

Suddenly, Mrs Gordon began to cry.

Then . . . .

They searched for him, but he was gone."

Fay told Mrs Gordon to get dressed.

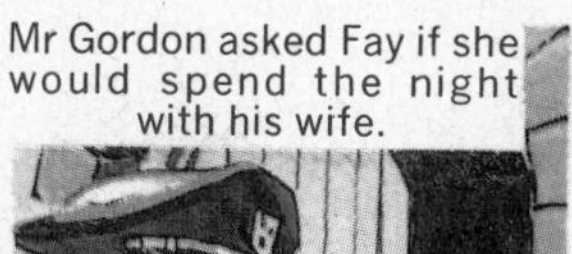

Later that night...

THIS REALLY IS A BAD STORM. WHAT IF MRS GORDON'S DREAM WAS TRUE? OH, NOW I'M BEING SILLY!

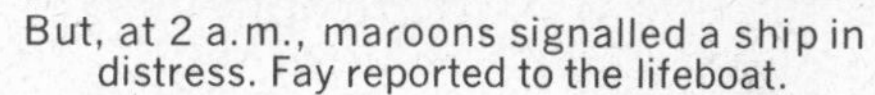
But, at 2 a.m., maroons signalled a ship in distress. Fay reported to the lifeboat.

TRY THIS COLOURFUL HOBBY

All the leaves shown in this page are from trees easily found in Britain. They are good leaves to use for leaf prints, as they are simple shapes.

LEAF-PRINTING

LEAF printing is a simple and interesting way of making designs with many uses. You will need some tubes of designers' colour which can be bought at any artists' supply shop or a good stationer's.

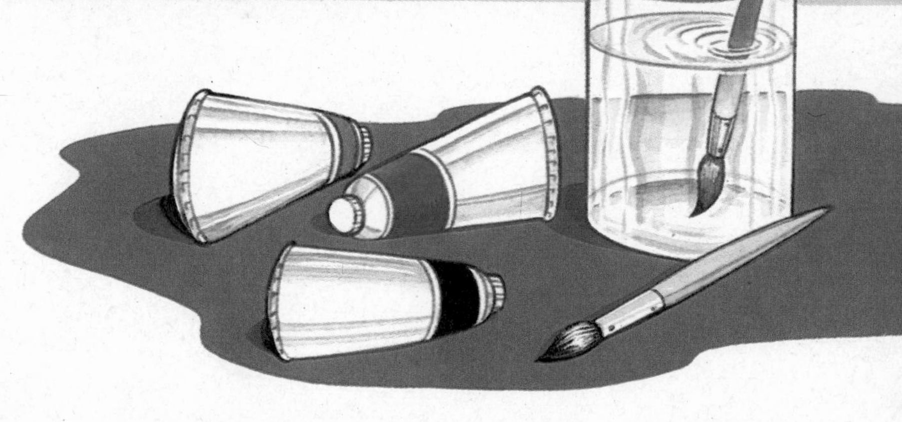

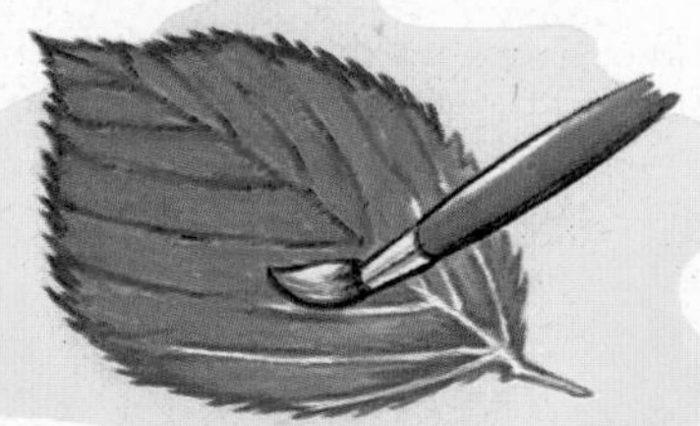

Make sure the paint is thick enough to be fairly sticky. Paint the veins of the leaf only. Do this carefully, but quickly, so the paint does not dry before you place the leaf on the paper.

On the left you can see how the leaf is carefully laid on the paper and pressed down firmly. Now, paint round the edge of the leaf quite freely. The leaf is then carefully peeled off the paper as shown on the right, leaving the finished print.

This is what the finished result looks like. The leaf print is all white, except for the veins.

The above print was made by painting the veins and the edge of the leaf itself, giving coloured edges, as well as veins.

To get this plain "silhouette" print, simply lay the leaf down flat and paint round the edge.

Here are three examples of how you can use leaf-printing. A book cover, a name plate in a book, or on the outside of a jewel box. There are many more uses for your prints — see how many you can think up.

THE DREAMS OF ALWYN

ALWYN ADAMS often has vivid dreams that have a strange way of coming true. One winter's night she has an unseasonable dream.

There was no school that day, and Alwyn hurried down to Ricky Rogers' studio.
CRUMBS! LOOK AT ALL THE GIRLS WHO WANT TO MODEL FOR RICKY ROGERS! HOW DO I GET NEAR ENOUGH TO MR ROGERS FOR HIM TO CHOOSE ME?
Alwyn went round to the back of the building.
I'VE GOT THE WINDOW OPEN. THIS IS THE WAY I'LL GO IN!
HOI! WHAT ARE YOU DOING?
OH! ER—I'M GOING WITH MR ROGERS TO THE BAHAMAS!
FIRST I'VE HEARD OF IT! COME ON, OUT!
Alwyn suddenly wriggled out of the coat.
HEY! COME BACK!
IT WOULD TAKE TOO LONG TO EXPLAIN! AH, THERE'S THE STUDIO! IN I GO!

In the studio, Ricky Rogers was talking to an assistant.
THAT'S A PHOTOGRAPH I TOOK ON A PREVIOUS VISIT TO THE BAHAMAS. THE MODEL IN THE PICTURE IS THE SORT OF GIRL I'M LOOKING FOR.
OK, RICKY. I'LL START SORTING OUT THE APPLICANTS.

THAT ATTENDANT IS AFTER ME AGAIN! I'VE GOT TO FIND RICKY ROGERS IN A HURRY!
Alwyn didn't notice the lighting cables snaking across the floor.
She tripped and went headlong through the photograph!
HELP!
OO—ER! I'VE STUCK MY HEAD THROUGH THE PHOTOGRAPH! LOOK AT THAT REFLECTION IN THE MIRROR! IT'S THE SCENE I DREAMED ABOUT!
MY LOVELY PHOTOGRAPH! SHE'S RUINED IT!

OW! I ONLY WANTED TO ASK YOU ABOUT A MODELLING JOB IN THE BAHAMAS, MR ROGERS!
OVER MY DEAD BODY! CHUCK HER OUT, FRED!

SHE'S BEEN TRYING TO JUMP THE QUEUE, THAT'S WHAT!
WHAT'S GOING ON? WHERE DID SHE COME FROM?
JUMPING THE QUEUE? SHE'S GOT A NERVE! GET HER, GIRLS!
OUCH!
OH, CRUMBS! I'M NOT GETTING TO THE SUNSHINE, BUT I'M CERTAINLY HAVING A HOT TIME!

Out and

THERE'S really only one way to enjoy the countryside to the full and that is on your own two feet. You can SEE it by car, but you can only see, smell, hear and be part of it by walking. When you go depends on you—each season has its charms—but how you go is something else again. Here are a few hints that should add to the enjoyment of your walks.

If you go for long walks on rough ground, it's safer to wear boots. Walking boots can be painful on your purse, but not as painful as a broken or sprained ankle. Slacks—not jeans—are best if you are walking amongst undergrowth or if the weather is cold. Two thin jerseys are warmer than one thick one and make it easier to ring the changes. An anorak is essential for hill walking. There are many different kinds, so choose carefully.

Have everything inside your rucksack. Nothing should be hanging outside it or carried in the hands. With the new type of "high-pack" rucksacks, the weight is kept nearer the top. Remember to have the things you need quickly at the top. Pack in reverse order what you'll need—bedding in last. Be careful no hard corners dig into your back. Straps are provided to carry a ground-sheet at the top and a tent at the bottom of your rucksack.

About

Camping is probably the cheapest way of staying overnight—but it needs careful planning if you're to be comfortable. Pitch your tent on level ground in a sheltered spot near drinking water, and make sure you have privacy.

The Youth Hostels Association provides another method of living cheaply on a walking tour. When you join, buy a booklet and study the rules. It's amazing how much easier life is in a hostel if you know the ropes, and reading the booklet will tell you all you want to know.

Here are a few address of organisations that will be only too willing to help you get out and about.

The Camping Club, 11 Lower Grosvenor Place, London, S.W.1.

Ramblers' Association, 124 Finchley Road, London, N.W.3.

Youth Hostels Association, Trevelyan House, St Albans, Herts.

National Parks Commission, 1 Cambridge Gate, Regents Park, London, N.W.1.

BEAUTY—THE ROMAN WAY

ROMAN girls would envy the modern age for its skill in producing beauty aids, but 20th-century girls would not have much to teach them about making the most of their appearance.

To improve her complexion, a Roman girl slept with a flour-and-milk paste smeared thickly over her face. When she awoke, slave girls brought bowls of scented water to wash off the paste.

The paste removed, the Roman lady sat back and waited for her slaves to put on her make-up, which was kept in pretty little boxes and caskets not unlike the ones you have.

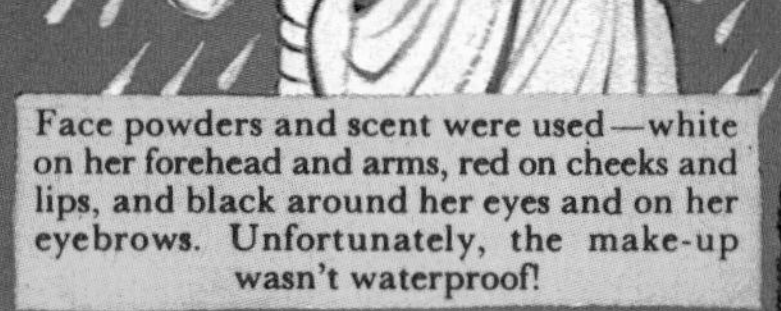

Face powders and scent were used—white on her forehead and arms, red on cheeks and lips, and black around her eyes and on her eyebrows. Unfortunately, the make-up wasn't waterproof!

After her make-up had been applied, it was bath-time for the Roman girl. Sometimes she bathed in asses' milk instead of water.

The bathing over, the whole process of applying her make-up began again.

Roman girls' hairstyles were very elaborate and took hours to arrange. However, many girls used wigs made from imported hair, some of it even coming from Britain.

Some Roman girls relied upon an enormous display of heavy jewellery to make them beautiful. In fact, many tended to overload themselves with jewels.

Take four ounces of incense and nitre. Add an ounce of gum from the bark of a tree and a cube of oily myrrh. Crush together and press through a sieve. Mix the resultant powder with honey. Add a handful of dried rose-leaves, some sal-ammoniac and frankincense. Pour on barley water, mix all together and apply the mixture.

So it seems that, despite two thousand years, the problems of beauty are much the same.

THE SWAMP SCHOOL SIEGE
AWAY back in the Middle Ages, some titled gent or other built himself a castle on the safest site he could find—on a rocky island in the middle of a swamp.
Nowadays, it houses Miss Green's Academy for Girls, known locally, of course, as the Swamp School. The only way to reach it across the swamp is by following the marker flags, and a bespectacled city gent is fast approaching by that route . . .
The man was the lawyer representing Sir Jasper Trout, from whom the school was rented.
. . . THERE IT IS, MISS GREEN— BUY OR GET OUT.
CAN YOU GIVE ME TEN DAYS' GRACE?
The lawyer refused the request, so Miss Green called the senior girls together.
. . . SO YOU SEE, GIRLS, IN TEN DAYS' TIME A LEGACY BECOMES DUE WHICH WOULD ENABLE US TO BUY THE BUILDING.
THE TROUBLE IS, SIR JASPER WANTS US OUT TOMORROW. HOWEVER, I HAVE A PLAN . . .

Plenty of food and other necessities were taken to the school, then the girls uprooted their link with the outside world—the flags!
SOME OF THE JUNIORS WANT TO KNOW HOW WE GET OUT AGAIN, JANE.
ONLY MISS GREEN KNOWS THAT!

But next day Sir Jasper and his men were not deterred by the lack of marker flags.
FOLLOW ME, MEN!
GET INTO THAT BUILDING AND THROW OUT EVERY DESK, CHAIR, TABLE AND BED!
SURE, BOSS. IT'LL BE EASY!
But a few soggy steps later, up to their waists in mud, Sir Jasper's strong-arm men weren't so sure!
HELP! WE'RE SINKING!
Luckily, one of them had brought a rope, and hauled the others to safety.
THIS SWAMP WON'T STOP ME!

So, early next morning, Sir Jasper was back—with mechanical help!
LOOK! A TRACTOR WITH BIG BALLOON TYRES!
IT'LL CROSS THE SWAMP AS IF IT WERE DRY LAND!
ARCHERY TEAM, READY...
Unfortunately for the landlord, he hadn't checked up on the Academy archery team. They were Inter-School Champions.
FIRE!
In the whistling of an arrow, he was as deflated as his own balloon tyres! Four direct hits torpedoed the tractor on the edge of the swamp, and down it went.

During the course of the next eight days, Sir Jasper Trout racked his brains for some way of getting into that school. He tried laying planks, but they sank. He tried flying in by balloon, but it was blown off course. He tried firing harpoons to firm land, but the girls cut the ropes. It seemed hopeless.

A close examination revealed a message strapped to a wing of the strange carrier pigeon. It instructed the manager to purchase the school . . .
FOR YOU, SIR JASPER. TITLE DEEDS, I BELIEVE, SIR.
I DON'T KNOW HOW YOU MANAGED THAT, MISS GREEN, BUT YOU ARE STILL IN A FIX! YOU CAN'T GET OUT!
OH, CAN'T WE?

LEFT A BIT, MAY; ON A BIT, JENNY...

ALL RIGHT! YOU'VE WON! HOW DID YOU DO IT?
SIMPLE! JUNE PHOTOGRAPHED THE POSITION OF THE FLAGS BEFORE WE TOOK THEM OUT. ONE THING WE INSIST ON IS THAT GIRLS MAKE THE MOST OF THEIR FAVOURITE HOBBIES. YOU WERE BEATEN BY WELL-USED LEISURE TIME, SIR JASPER!

MAKE YOUR OWN MATCH

THIS little moorland cottag is made from two larg match-boxes; brown, blue an yellow cartridge paper; a sma rubber erase several use matches; a sho box lid; post paint; glue; piece of twig.

Take the inside trays out of the two match-boxes and glue the flaps together, one pair inside the other pair. Next, cut two pieces of brown paper into the shapes shown to make the ends of the cottage. Cover the front an back with cartridge paper (or pieces of postcard, painted brown) cut to size. Th door is made from blue paper and th windows from yellow paper. Glue them o

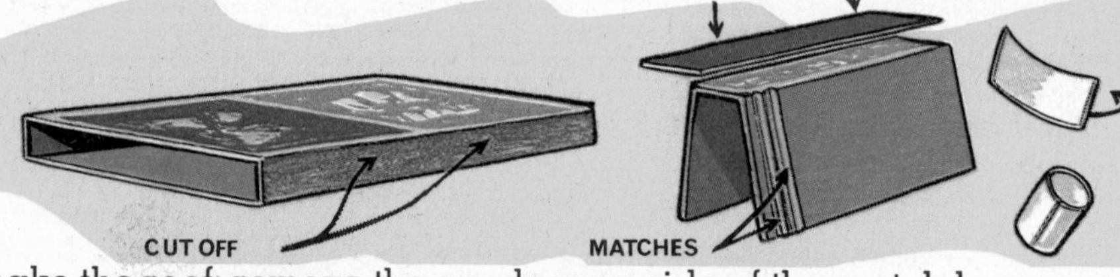

To make the roof, remove the sandpaper side of the match-box cover. Paint the big sides pale brown and glue on lengths of matchsticks to give a timbered roof effect. Glue the strip of brown paper on top. Finally, make a small roll of white paper for the chimney, glue it on, paint it, and glue the roof in position on the cottage.

Make the tree from a twig of evergreen. Take a rubber eraser and push a hole in it with the sharp point of your school compasses, or a slender nail. Now, cut a piece of paper shaped like 'a', tall enough to hide the rubber when it is finally wrapped around. Next, make a circl of brown paper 'b' with a "v" cut into it. Pus your "tree" into the hole in the rubber, glu shape 'b' around the top, and finally wra shape 'a' round it all.

The well roof is a piece of white paper folded in the middle and painted red. The wall is brown paper rolled into a tube, and three matchsticks make the framework. The roof is then glued on, and slates painted, to complete the effect.

The reeds. Cut out the shape on the left. Paint the inside yellow. Wrap it into a tube and paint the outside green.

The base is made from the shoe - box lid, with brown cartridge paper glued on top. First, paint the grass on, leaving gaps for the cobble stones. When the grass is dry, paint in the cobbles, and glue down a piece of silver paper for the pond.

Finally, glue everything down on to the base, including a small match-stick fence around the pond, with cotton for fence wire. Perhaps you could design other buildings and features yourself to add to your little model.

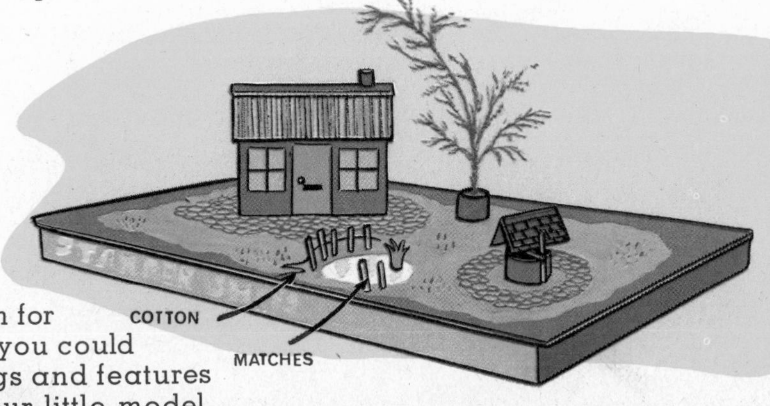

CALEN
CUST

Up-Helly-Aa is held at Lerwick, in Shetland, on the last day of Yuletide. These festivities originated during the Norse occupation and they symbolise the triumph of the sun over the long winter nights. The most impressive part of the ceremony is the burning of a large model of a Viking ship, the crew of which all wear Viking dress.

No one knows the origin of the dance performed by "The Nutters" at Bacup, in Lancashire. The eight men get their title from the wooden "nuts" which are part of the costume.

DRUID CEREMONY

The Druid Order still celebrates the return of spring and the new season of growth. The rites are performed near the site of an ancient burial ground at Tower Hill, London.

If you go to Minehead, in Somerset, you may s this ancient ceremony. A strangely-design "Hobby Horse", with a body of painted canvas prances to the sound of music

R OF
OMS

BRITAIN is a land steeped in history, tradition and customs. Many of these customs date back to before the Middle Ages, yet have survived to the present day. On these pages we show a few from different parts of the country.

CHEESE ROLLING

This takes place in the evening at Cooper's Hill, near Birdlip, in Gloucester. At the signal from the starter, a large cheese in a wooden case is rolled down the hill, pursued by the village boys.

JUL
16

The Annual Swan-Upping ceremony is held on the River Thames between London and Henley, during which all the Thames swans are identified by members of the Dyers and the Vintners Companies of London.

SEP
8

The Horn Dance, symbolic of an ancient deer ceremony, is held at Abbot's Bromley, in Staffordshire.

Hogmanay Flambeaux Procession is held at Comrie, in Perthshire. Pipers lead torch-bearers to the main square, where merrymaking continues until well into the morning.

SKINFLINT SCHOOL
MARCH WIND SCHOOL
EBENEZER SCRAPE is the miserly headmaster of March Wind School for Girls. He won't part with a penny if he can help it, as his pupils know to their cost.
One afternoon, Mr Scrape was busying himself with his favourite hobby—money.
ONLY ONE HUNDRED POUNDS, NINETEEN AND SIXPENCE-HALFPENNY IN PETTY CASH! OH, GRACIOUS ME! THE LOWEST TOTAL YET! THIS WILL NOT DO AT ALL! I MUST GET MORE MONEY! BUT HOW?
HEH! HEH! HEH! BY JOVE, I'VE GOT IT! THE GIRLS HAVE ALL JUST RECEIVED THEIR TERM'S POCKET-MONEY FROM THEIR PARENTS. THEY MUST BE PERSUADED TO PART WITH IT!

Next day...
I HOPE YOU'LL ALL SUPPORT THIS VENTURE.
A SCHOOL EXCURSION!
EXCURSION TO FILM SHOW IN MIDDLETON THIS FRIDAY. TRANSPORT & MEAL INCLUSIVE JUST 8/6 per HEAD
THE OLD SKINFLINT MUST BE UP TO SOMETHING.
THERE MUST BE A CATCH, CHRISTINE, BUT WE MIGHT AS WELL GO TO KEEP AN EYE ON MR SCRAPE.
THANK YOU, MY DEAR.
The day of the excursion arrived.
OUR TRANSPORT SHOULD BE HERE ANY MINUTE, GIRLS.
AH, YES! HERE IT COMES!
SURELY NOT THAT HORSE AND CART!
G-GOOD GRIEF!
WE'VE BEEN STUNG!
AH, THIS IS THE WAY TO TRAVEL!
YES—CHEAPLY!
THIS IS AWFUL!
STILL, THE FILM AND THE MEAL SHOULD MAKE UP FOR THIS INDIGNITY.

But, long before the cart reached Middleton, it turned into a field.
MR SCRAPE! I THOUGHT WE WERE GOING TO THE CINEMA IN MIDDLETON!
BUT THIS IS MIDDLETON—MIDDLETON FARM!
IN YOU GO, GIRLS! THE FILM SHOW WILL COMMENCE SHORTLY.
OH, HAPPY, HAPPY DAY! WHAT A LOT OF MONEY I'M GOING TO MAKE!
HUH! SOME CINEMA! THE OLD MISER'S TRICKED US AGAIN! HE ONLY WANTED OUR POCKET-MONEY!
In the barn . . .
WHAT ABOUT THE MEAL WE PAID FOR, SIR?
AH, WELL...YES! THAT IS IN MY CAPABLE HANDS!
BUT, SIR! WE'RE ALL STARVING—AND WE PAID FOR FOOD!
HERE'S YOUR MEAL—OATMEAL! TAKE A POCKETFUL EACH. YOU CAN MAKE PORRIDGE FROM IT TOMORROW. HEH! HEH!
AND TO THINK WE FELL FOR IT!
POPPY! FORGET YOUR STOMACH AND FEED YOUR MIND! THE FILM SHOW'S ABOUT TO BEGIN.
I THOUGHT HE WAS ONLY INTERESTED IN FISHING FOR MONEY!
PEPPERMINT ROCK! BET HE'S WISHING HE WERE HOLDING THE ROYAL MINT!

At last the show was over, and, on the way back to school...
MR SCRAPE, WE'D LIKE TO BUY SOME STRAWBERRIES.
NO, POPPY! YOU'RE NOT TO WASTE YOUR MONEY ON FRIPPERIES!
STRAWBERRIES FOR SALE
THERE'S ONLY ONE WAY TO MAKE MR SCRAPE STOP—DROP A PENNY!
WHASSAT? MONEY? DRIVER! STOP THIS INSTANT!
While Mr Scrape feverishly hunted for the money, two girls sneaked off to buy the strawberries.
IT MUST BE HERE! I DISTINCTLY HEARD A COIN FALL!
PERHAPS IT'S UNDER THE HORSE'S HOOVES.
AH, YES!
Mr Scrape slapped the horse hard—and it bolted.
WOW!

Finally . . .

Later. . . .

JUMPING JACK

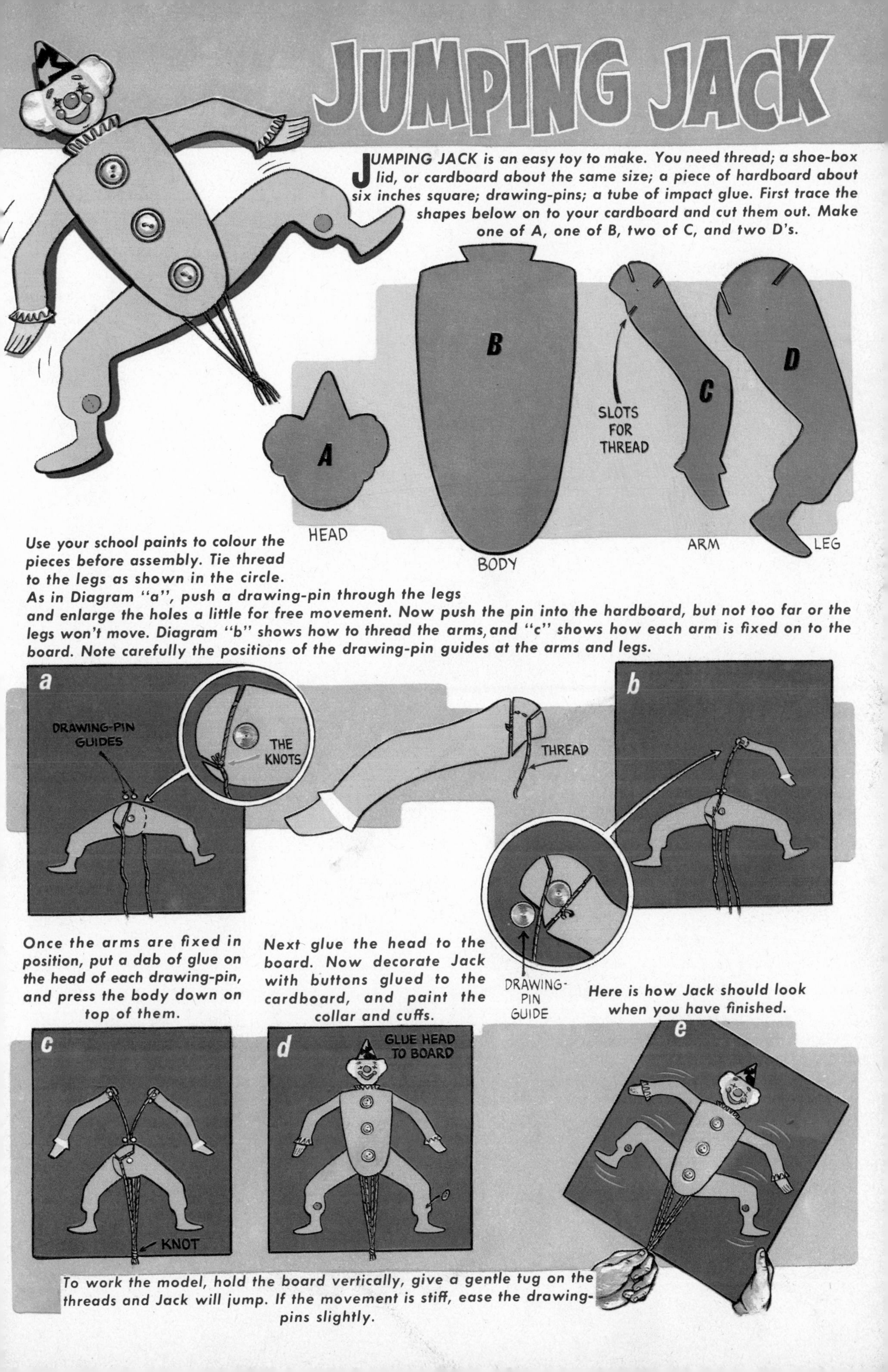

JUMPING JACK is an easy toy to make. You need thread; a shoe-box lid, or cardboard about the same size; a piece of hardboard about six inches square; drawing-pins; a tube of impact glue. First trace the shapes below on to your cardboard and cut them out. Make one of A, one of B, two of C, and two D's.

Use your school paints to colour the pieces before assembly. Tie thread to the legs as shown in the circle. As in Diagram "a", push a drawing-pin through the legs and enlarge the holes a little for free movement. Now push the pin into the hardboard, but not too far or the legs won't move. Diagram "b" shows how to thread the arms, and "c" shows how each arm is fixed on to the board. Note carefully the positions of the drawing-pin guides at the arms and legs.

Once the arms are fixed in position, put a dab of glue on the head of each drawing-pin, and press the body down on top of them.

Next glue the head to the board. Now decorate Jack with buttons glued to the cardboard, and paint the collar and cuffs.

Here is how Jack should look when you have finished.

To work the model, hold the board vertically, give a gentle tug on the threads and Jack will jump. If the movement is stiff, ease the drawing-pins slightly.

I wait in the wings
While the orchestra strings,
Tuning up, fill the theatre with sound;
While the dancers, all set,
Try a last pirouette,
Midst the bustle that sweeps all around.
I wait in the wings,
Think of millions of things—
Of my steps, of my dress, of my cues;
Think of props, of the light,
That it's opening night,
That it's too late to relace my shoes.
I wait in the wings
As the last call-bell rings,
Then the slow-dimming house-lights are gone.
One more chord. Here I go!
Then I suddenly know
It's the moment I've longed for—I'M ON!

Bobby Dazzler

BOBBY DAZZLER is the only girl at Westbury School for Boys, where her mother is matron. One day their P.E. teacher, Mr Dudley, pays a visit to the common room.

HANG ON, MIKE! I'M COMING!
HELP!
QU...QU...QUICK!
ALL RIGHT, I'VE GOT THE REINS!

A GOOD PIECE OF TRICK RIDING, WASN'T IT, BOBBY? I EVEN CONVINCED YOU I WAS FRIGHTENED.
I GIVE UP!

Mike and Bobby rejoined the party and they set off.
WE'RE COMING TO A STREAM THAT HAS TO BE FORDED, SO BE CAREFUL.
WHEN BOBBY IS CROSSING THE STREAM, I'LL DRAW LEVEL WITH HER AND UNFASTEN HER SADDLE SO THAT SHE FALLS IN.
GREAT IDEA, MIKE!
But as Mike leaned over, he slipped.
WAA!

HO! HO! HO!
OH, IT'S VERY FUNNY, ISN'T IT? IF YOU DON'T SHUT UP I'LL...I'LL...
I SHOULD HAVE THOUGHT THAT WATER WOULD HAVE COOLED YOU DOWN, MIKE!
The party started off again.
MAY WE STOP FOR OUR PICNIC, SIR?
YES, BOBBY. THIS LOOKS LIKE A NICE SPOT—AND MIKE WILL GET A CHANCE TO DRY OUT.
THIS IS THE LIFE! I THINK I'LL BE A COWBOY. I COULD LIE ON THE PRAIRIES EVERY DAY, HAVING MY SIESTA. THAT MEANS A SNOOZE, BOBBY!
I'LL PUT YOU TO SLEEP WITH A ROCK IF YOU DON'T BE QUIET, MIKE!

RIGHT, THAT DOES IT! I'LL SHOW YOU THAT I'M A GOOD HORSEMAN!
MIKE, SIT DOWN. YOU CAN'T GO RIDING ROUND THE COUNTRYSIDE IN A HORSE BLANKET!

LET HIM GO, BOBBY. HE'LL SOON BE BACK.
But Mike hadn't reappeared by the time the trek started again.
BOBBY—GO AND SEE WHAT MIKE NORTON'S UP TO. WE'LL TAKE IT EASY TO LET YOU CATCH UP.

When Bobby reached the edge of the wood that Mike had entered . . .
THAT'S MIKE'S PONY, BUT WHERE'S MIKE? AND THERE'S SMOKE OVER THERE. I'D BETTER GO AND SEE WHAT'S HAPPENING!

BOBBY! THE HORSE THREW ME AND I'VE HURT MY ANKLE! I CAN'T MOVE! I LIT A FIRE TO ATTRACT ATTENTION!
AND THE FIRE'S SPREADING! I'D BETTER GET YOU OUT OF HERE!

GO AND GET HELP, MIKE! THIS FIRE'S GETTING SERIOUS!
OK!

Bobby grabbed a fire-fighting broom.
I HOPE MIKE HURRIES BACK WITH HELP! IT'S SPREADING TOO FAST FOR ME TO COPE WITH IT!
Help soon came.
THERE ARE SOME MORE BROOMS OVER THERE!

THERE'S A BIT OVER THERE, BOBBY! BRIAN— TO YOUR LEFT A BIT.

At last the fire was out.
THAT WAS QUICK THINKING, BOBBY! THE FIRE COULD HAVE BEEN DANGEROUS.
OF COURSE, IT WAS MY GALLOPING FOR HELP THAT REALLY PREVENTED ANY SERIOUS DAMAGE.
YES, MIKE, YOU'RE A REAL BALL OF FIRE!

BESS

IT was a dark, wet, blustery night, and Sue pulled up her coat collar and quickened her footsteps. It was then that she became aware of a vague shadow at her heels.

Turning quickly, she found a young dog gazing at her pathetically, at the same time cringing away from the blow it had obviously come to expect. Tied to its collar was an old piece of rope, its frayed end trailing on the damp pavement. After this first quick glance, Sue hardened her heart and hurried on, for she knew that she could not expect even her mother to take in yet another animal.

Their family consisted of father, mother and three children, of whom Sue, at eleven, was the eldest. Then there was Suki, a lovable little black-and-tan terrier with a smooth, wavy coat and long, fluffy tail.

In her youth, she had been mother to fourteen puppies, but was now ten years old, and a very important member of the family.

The way in which she not only accepted, but actually mothered, the various assortment of birds and animals that were given temporary lodging in the household, was a source of constant amazement to those who did not know her very well.

The seventh member of the family was Frisky, a black-and-white cat that had been rescued from the gutter when only a few weeks old and near starvation.

Feeling that it would really be kinder to the puppy to ignore it completely, rather than give it encouragement which could only end in dreadful disappointment, she hurried along.

However, the fact that this encounter had, so far, not been unfriendly, was obviously encouragement enough to the animal, and it trotted along at Sue's heels, practically tripping her at every step.

" Why," thought Sue, " do these things always have to happen to our family? Other people are not constantly finding stray animals and being made to feel guilty and miserable as a result."

As she turned to go into the gate of her home, the dog sat down and looked at her pleadingly. Sue bent to stroke it, and immediately the dog jumped to lick her face, putting both front paws around her neck, whimpering and quivering with friendliness.

Sue's mind was made up ! When her father answered her knock, there was the dog sitting at her heels, desperately hoping for a friendly welcome.

" You can take that back to where you found it," said her father, pointing to the bedraggled figure.

" Oh, please, Daddy, do let her in for tonight," pleaded Sue. " She's so miserable."

By this time, Sue's mother had come to see what was happening, and Sue turned to her, hoping to see the pity she expected to find.

During the discussion that followed, the puppy sat at Sue's feet, terrified of losing contact with this new-found friend. She was tan in colour, with a white chest, black muzzle and beautiful liquid brown eyes that gazed soulfully at each of them in turn.

One ear permanently cocked, gave her an air of constant inquiry. Although she was obviously young, she was already bigger than Suki, who, after giving a warning growl, was now trying to wash some of the dirt from this stranger.

Sue's mother stooped to see if there was a name on the dog's collar and, as she did so, two paws went around her neck and a soft muzzle pushed into her shoulder.

She looked at her husband, and it was silently agreed that the dog should have food and a bed for the night.

A DECISION

THE next day was Sunday, and each member of the household was greeted ecstatically by the overnight visitor. They all laughed at her clumsiness. Her feet seemed to go in all directions, and she trundled through anything that happened to be in her path.

She obviously had never seen stairs before, and had no idea as to how she should climb them. After looking at them in surprise, she watched various members of the family run up them, and then tried to follow, only to land in a sprawling heap, an expression of hurt amazement on her face.

The previous night it had been agreed that Sue should take the dog to the Police Station, and although she secretly hoped that her parents would change their minds, they insisted that she kept her promise.

So, after breakfast, Sue fastened Suki's lead to the stray's collar and, fighting back the tears, started off. She made the journey last as long as possible, but eventually handed the reluctant animal to the police sergeant.

As she walked slowly home through the park, a long-drawn, blood-curdling howl came from behind her and she knew without doubt that it was " her " dog that was making this fearful noise.

She put her hands over her ears and ran, but she could not blot out the sounds of utter misery that followed her.

She spent the rest of the morning in her bedroom and, after picking at lunch, took Suki for a walk. Nothing seemed to help her forget her heart-rending experience of the morning. She was near to tears.

That evening, as the family sat around the fire, the sitting-room door was suddenly thrown open. Startled, they all turned, half expecting to see a stranger in the doorway. Then came the unbelieving gasps.

There, managing somehow to look both apprehensive and pleased, stood the dog they all thought to be locked up in the Police Station.

" However did she manage to get in here?" said Mother wonderingly. She went into the kitchen and found the door to the garden wide open. There was no doubt about it—the dog had not only managed to find her way from the Police Station, but had also opened the doors by pulling down the handles.

The children glanced at their parents, then they watched as their father, acknowledging defeat, went to the cupboard to prepare a meal for the dog. Delightedly, they embraced this new member of the family, and argued over a name, finally deciding to call her " Bess."

Next day she was bathed, groomed and given a new lead and collar. Father had been in touch with the police and now she was really theirs !

Once accepted by the family she had adopted, Bess settled in as though she had known no other life. It was obvious that she had not been used to restrictions or living indoors, and this led the family to believe that she had probably belonged to a band of gipsies who had recently been staying in the neighbourhood.

But she was very intelligent, and they were confident that they would soon be able to train her and have another animal who was as well-behaved as Suki.

It soon became evident that she was a cross-bred Boxer, a variety of dog renowned for being practically untrainable! Certainly, she learnt very early to sit to command and wait patiently to be fed, looking as though butter would not melt in her mouth. Just as certainly, she could not be left to herself for five minutes before proceeding to wreck the house!

She loved human beings and was not content to lie on the carpet, but would manage to slither, almost unnoticeably, on to whichever lap looked most inviting at that particular moment, where she would do her best to convince herself, and the lap's owner, that she was a Pekinese and therefore quite entitled to that position.

She never seemed to lose the clumsiness that had been so noticeable on that first night, and would sprawl inelegantly on her nose, legs splayed in every direction, as she fell up the stairs. Yet, in spite of this, and her bulk, she could run like the wind and no other dog ever managed to keep up with her on her outings to the local parks and commons.

She had wrestling matches with the children, from which they all emerged worn-out, no one knowing who was the victor. She had her favourite toys, with which she would play for hours, tirelessly throwing rubber balls and bones into the air and catching them. Before long, she had won over every member of the family.

It was about this time that Bess started to roam. She would let herself out of the back door and disappear for hours. Occasionally there would be reports of her visiting friends of the family, but usually she seemed to vanish without trace.

On her return, she would open the door and slink through the house as stealthily as any cat-burglar, the only traces of her return being open doors and, perhaps, a trail of muddy footprints.

THE GIPSIES

ONE day, Sue was taking the dogs for a run across the Common, when she noticed that the gipsies were back again. As they neared the encampment, Suki growled. Bess, however, became excited, giving short, sharp barks and ran from the gipsies to Sue and back again.

Suddenly she ran towards a horse standing at the edge of the camp.

Sue called to Bess, thinking that the horse would take fright, but to her surprise the horse whinnied and nuzzled the dog.

Then Sue saw a tiny foal lying beside the mare.

" Get out of there, you !" shouted a ragged, untidy figure who emerged from the caravan. He stooped to pick up a clod of earth.

" Don't dare throw that at my dog !" said Sue, sounding braver than she felt.

" Your dog ?" he said. " Huh, it was my dog before you stole it ! I've a good mind to have the police on you !"

Sue reached out for Bess's collar and, as she did so, the man moved threateningly towards them. Bess growled menacingly and, as the man came on, she hurled herself towards him. The gipsy kicked out at her and Bess yelped and grabbed his leg in her strong, white teeth.

Fortunately, the man was wearing thick corduroy trousers and big heavy boots, so that very little damage was done.

He grabbed a piece of iron to throw at the dog. It missed and struck the mare. She gave a terrified neigh and shied, and the foal at her side scrambled to her feet in alarm.

By this time both dogs were barking and snapping around the man's feet. He now had a whip, and was lashing furiously in all directions, while the various mongrels tied up around the vans added to the confusion.

Sue was terrified, and was on the point of running for help when a voice from behind her said:

" Well now, what's going on here ?" and, turning, she found to her relief and amazement a policeman, who, she afterwards heard, had been sent to investigate the camp after complaints of theft from the local residents.

The policeman told Sue to sit with his companion in the patrol car.

Briefly she told him what had happened. After a few moments, he left her and walked over to examine the mare, and on returning told Sue that they would get in touch with the R.S.P.C.A. regarding the animals on the encampment.

Later Sue arrived home and poured out the story of her adventure to the rest of the family.

Her parents were naturally concerned, but the children were rather envious of her experience, and she really felt quite heroic.

A few days later, the friendly policeman called to let her know that the gipsy's animals had been taken into the care of the R.S.P.C.A., who had placed the mare and her foal in a field not far from Sue's home.

In the months that followed, she sometimes walked with the dogs to visit the mare and her foal, who soon recovered from the effects of the life they had been forced to endure.

On these visits, Bess and the mare were overjoyed to see one another again, and Sue hated to part them when it was time to leave.

Bess still had that naughty streak which seemed to compel her to do wrong, but afterwards she was so full of abject apology and love that she is, to this day, still living with the family.

Although, curiously enough, once she knew that the mare was happily settled, away from the gipsies, she stopped roaming, from which the family knew that she must have sensed their return to the district and wanted her companion to enjoy the same kind of loving home which she herself had found.

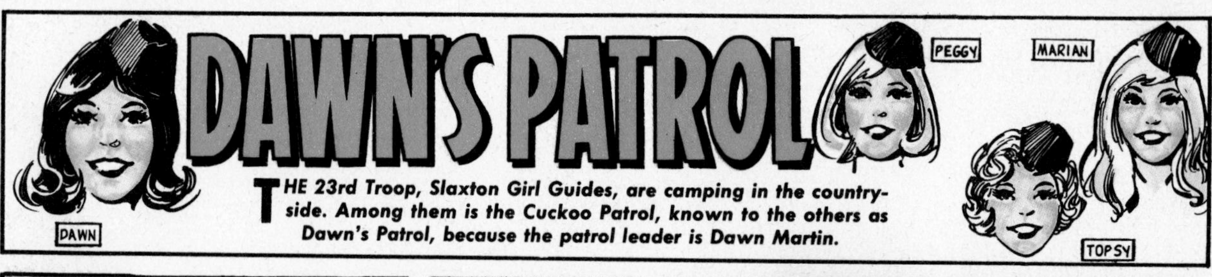
DAWN'S PATROL
PEGGY
MARIAN
DAWN
TOPSY
THE 23rd Troop, Slaxton Girl Guides, are camping in the countryside. Among them is the Cuckoo Patrol, known to the others as Dawn's Patrol, because the patrol leader is Dawn Martin.

TOMORROW THERE WILL BE A TRACKING COMPETITION AMONG ALL THE GUIDE TROOPS CAMPING IN THE AREA. THERE IS NO NEED TO FOLLOW THE TRACK-MARKER EXACTLY. ALL WE WANT YOU TO DO IS FIND OUT WHICH ROUTE SHE HAS TAKEN AND MARK IT ON A MAP.

TODAY WE ARE ALLOWED A PRACTICE SESSION OVER THE AREA TO BE USED. JENNY IS GOING TO LAY THE TRACK. GIVE HER TWENTY MINUTES' START, THEN OFF YOU GO.
OH, GOSH! I DON'T MUCH FANCY TWO SESSIONS LIKE THIS, DAWN
NO MORE DO I, PEGGY.

I'VE GOT A PLAN THAT WILL SAVE US ONE JOURNEY AND PROBABLY WIN US THE COMPETITION, TOO!
LET'S HEAR IT, THEN!
ANYTHING FOR AN EASY LIFE!

Marian explained her plan and, twenty minutes later, when the "hounds" set off at a run, Dawn's patrol took it easy.
WHAT'S WRONG WITH YOU? TOO MUCH BREAKFAST AGAIN?
THEY'RE STILL ASLEEP!
THEY CAN LAUGH NOW—BUT WE'LL HAVE THE LAST LAUGH TOMORROW.

During the morning, Dawn's Patrol seemed to be well off-track.
LOOK AT PEGGY—MILES AWAY FROM THE TRAIL!
WHAT DO YOU EXPECT? SHE'S IN DAWN'S PATROL!

Two hours passed.
THAT'S EVERYONE EXCEPT DAWN, PEGGY, MARIAN AND TOPSY.
I SUPPOSE WE'D BETTER TRACK THEM DOWN, TOO!
THEY'LL PROBABLY BE IN WALES NOW!

An hour later....
WHAT WAS IT LIKE IN TIMBUCTOO?
JUST WAIT TILL TOMORROW!

Next morning. . .
WELL, GIRLS, THE TRACK-LAYER HAS STARTED. OFF YOU GO, AND THE FIRST PATROL TO GIVE ME THE TRAIL MARKED OUT ON THE MAP WILL WIN. GOOD LUCK TO ALL OF YOU.

As the others streamed away....
AREN'T YOU FOUR ENTERING THE CONTEST?
OH, YES, MISS—WE'RE JUST TAKING OUR TIME.

Two hours later, the track-layer returned.
LOOK AT HER SHOES!
AND HER STOCKINGS!
THE SLEEVE OF HER TUNIC, TOO!

SAND IN HER SHOES, —LOOSE SAND.
WE ALL KNOW WHAT THAT MEANS.
THIS IS A PIECE OF CAKE!
THOSE FOUR ARE UP TO NO GOOD, I'M CERTAIN.

NOW, SHE MUST HAVE GONE THROUGH MACGREGOR'S COPSE...
...AND ACROSS SIMMOND'S MEADOW...
...THEN ON TO THE CROW WOOD...
...AND THROUGH FINNEY'S SPINNEY...

A few minutes later....
BACK ALREADY? SURELY YOU CAN'T...BUT...YES...YES...IT'S ABSOLUTELY CORRECT! WELL DONE!
HOW DID YOU DO IT, DAWN?

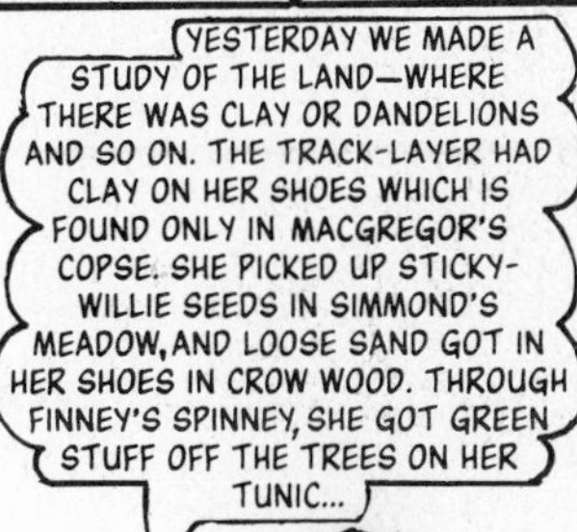
YESTERDAY WE MADE A STUDY OF THE LAND—WHERE THERE WAS CLAY OR DANDELIONS AND SO ON. THE TRACK-LAYER HAD CLAY ON HER SHOES WHICH IS FOUND ONLY IN MACGREGOR'S COPSE. SHE PICKED UP STICKY-WILLIE SEEDS IN SIMMOND'S MEADOW, AND LOOSE SAND GOT IN HER SHOES IN CROW WOOD. THROUGH FINNEY'S SPINNEY, SHE GOT GREEN STUFF OFF THE TREES ON HER TUNIC...

When Dawn finished her explanation. . .
BRILLIANT! YOU SHOULD BE DETECTIVES!

Later, at the prize-giving . . .
...BY A CLEVER PIECE OF WORK WHICH DESERVES THE HIGHEST PRAISE—AND THIS MAGNIFICENT TROPHY.
HEH-HEH! WHO'S LAUGHING NOW?

MADGE THE BADGER
YOUNG Madge Baker's favourite hobby is making badges—aided by her friend, Tina. One morning, Miss Blackie, headmistress of Brayton School, sends for them....
THIS IS OUR NEW GIRL, CLARE BRECK. SHE'LL BE IN YOUR CLASS, MADGE, AND I'D LIKE YOU AND TINA TO LOOK AFTER HER FOR A DAY OR TWO.
ER, YES, MISS BLACKIE.
CLARE BRECK? BUT SHE'S THE DAUGHTER OF SIR JASON BRECK— THE OWNER OF HARLINGTON MANOR! I WONDER WHY SHE'S COMING TO AN ORDINARY SCHOOL LIKE OURS!
In the playground . . .
IT MUST BE MARVELLOUS TO LIVE IN A PLACE LIKE HARLINGTON, CLARE.
IT IS-BUT WE CAN'T AFFORD TO STAY THERE! THE COST OF UPKEEP IS ENORMOUS AND, UNLESS A MIRACLE HAPPENS, IT LOOKS AS THOUGH WE SHALL HAVE TO SELL IT.
A week later, Clare invited Madge and Tina to tea . . .
CLARE! IT'S MAGNIFICENT! IT WOULD BE TERRIBLE IF YOU HAD TO LEAVE!
IT WOULD BREAK MY FATHER'S HEART. HIS FAMILY HAVE LIVED HERE FOR FIVE CENTURIES. IF ONLY MORE VISITORS WOULD TURN UP ON SUNDAYS!
HARLINGTON HALL OPEN TO PUBLIC SUNDAYS
Later, Sir Jason himself showed the girls round the Manor.
SO QUEEN ELIZABETH REALLY SLEPT HERE... HEY! WHAT'S THAT CLANKING NOISE?
OUR GHOST, OF COURSE!
DON'T BE SUCH A TEASE, CLARE! YOU KNOW IT'S ONLY THE RAFTERS CREAKING!
ALL THE SAME, IT GIVES ME AN IDEA!

Next day, when Tina called at Madge's house . . .
MADGE! WHAT ON EARTH...?
JUST MY PLAN TO LURE MORE VISITORS TO HARLINGTON MANOR THIS SUNDAY. THERE'S NOTHING LIKE A GHOST TO STIR UP PUBLIC INTEREST!
IS HARLINGTON MANOR HAUNTED?
At school on Friday, Madge and Tina distributed the badges.
THERE ARE PLENTY HERE. I WANT YOU ALL TO WEAR THEM AT THE LOCAL FLOWER SHOW TOMORROW, WHERE EVERYONE CAN SEE THEM.
MORE BADGES! CAN I HAVE ONE, MADGE?
So, at the flower show . . .
HARLINGTON MANOR HAUNTED? FANCY THAT!
LET'S GO ALONG THERE TOMORROW.
GARDEN
GOOD! OUR PLAN'S WORKING!
Unnoticed by Madge, an American couple were showing great interest in the badges . . .
A HAUNTED ENGLISH MANOR, ELVER! THAT COULD BE JUST THE ANSWER TO OUR PROBLEMS.
IT SURE COULD! WE MUST LOOK INTO THIS!

On the Sunday, a record number of visitors turned up at Harlington.
CHEER UP, DAD. WE MUST BE MAKING LOTS OF MONEY TODAY, THANKS TO MADGE AND HER BADGES!
I'M VERY GRATEFUL TO MADGE, BUT I'M AFRAID NOTHING CAN SAVE US NOW. THIS MORNING I DISCOVERED DRY ROT IN THE ROOF-THOUSANDS OF POUNDS WORTH OF DAMAGE!
OH, NO!
SIR JASON! AN AMERICAN GENTLEMAN WISHES TO SPEAK TO YOU IN THE HALL.
I'D BETTER SEE WHAT HE WANTS.
When all the visitors had left . . .
SO ALL OUR EFFORTS WERE IN VAIN! POOR CLARE!
THANKS FOR TRYING, ANYHOW. I HAVEN'T SEEN DAD FOR HOURS. I SUPPOSE HE'S MOPING SOMEWHERE BY HIMSELF.
Suddenly . . .
MADGE! CLARE! LOOK!

THAT FOOLED YOU, DIDN'T IT? COME ALONG, GIRLS—WE'RE GOING TO CELEBRATE!
YOU NEARLY SCARED US OUT OF OUR WITS! FANCY FEELING LIKE JOKES TODAY OF ALL DAYS!
Sir Jason led the mystified girls to the dining-room.
THE MAN WHO CALLED EARLIER—MR ELVER HANKS—WISHES TO START A HOTEL FOR AMERICAN VISITORS IN A TYPICAL OLD ENGLISH SETTING. HE HAS DECIDED THAT A HAUNTED MANOR WOULD BE THE VERY PLACE FOR HIS PROJECT.
BUT, DAD...! DOES THAT MEAN WE'RE SELLING HARLINGTON?
OF COURSE WE'RE NOT SELLING! HE'S GOING TO RENT THE WEST WING. AND WITH THE AMOUNT OF MONEY HE'S OFFERED ME, WE'LL BE ABLE TO MEND THE ROOF—AND STAY IN THE REST OF THE HOUSE FOR AS LONG AS WE LIVE! AND NOW—HOW ABOUT SOME FOOD?
Later . . .
TO THINK THAT IT WAS ONE OF YOUR BADGES, MADGE, THAT LURED ELVER HANKS TO HARLINGTON! HOW LUCKY FOR CLARE!
LUCKY FOR US, TOO! WE'VE BEEN INVITED TO VISIT THE MANOR WHENEVER WE LIKE!

POLLY AND HER PRAM
ONE DAY POLLY IS INVITED TO HER FRIEND, JUNE'S BIRTHDAY PARTY. SHE TAKES BABY ALONG IN THE PRAM...
HELLO, POLLY! GLAD YOU COULD COME!
HAPPY BIRTHDAY, JUNE! I HAD TO BRING BABY. MUM'S OUT...
JUNE HAD A SURPRISE FOR HER GUESTS.
MARVO, THE MARVELLOUS MAGICIAN, IS GOING TO ENTERTAIN US.
OH, SUPER! YOU'LL ENJOY THIS, BABY!

YOU SEE THIS EGG? WATCH IT CAREFULLY..
GOO!

... AND IT VANISHES.
BUT BABY HAD SEEN WHERE THE EGG HAD GONE..

...AND AIMED A BLOW.
CRUNCH!
URGH!

THAT BABY'S RUINED MY TRICK!

LOOK HERE! KEEP OUT OF MY ACT!

BABY GRABBED MARVO'S HANKIE.
MY FLAGS!
MY GOODNESS! BABY!

BABY SHOVED MARVO...
WOWEE!

...AND ALL HIS TRICKS SHOWERED AROUND HIM.
COME ON, BABY! IT'S TIME TO MAKE SOMETHING ELSE DISAPPEAR — US!

WEE SLAVEY
NELLIE PERKS is learning to be a maid in the Victorian household of Sir William Selby Smythe and his family. She is nearly always kept very busy.
FIRM STROKES, NELLIE! AND DON'T FORGET—ONE HUNDRED AT LEAST!
WHEN YOU'VE FINISHED, BRING UP THE HOT WATER FOR MY BATH, NELLIE.
YES, MISS FLORA. YES, MISS ALICE.

THAT'S THE YOUNG LADIES TAKEN CARE OF. NOW I'VE TO SCOUR THE PANS. WE'RE ALWAYS ON THE GO, AMY!
NEVER MIND, NELLIE, I THINK THERE'S A NICE SURPRISE COMING.
Just then, Lady Smythe came into the kitchen.
I HAVE TOLD THE MASTER OF YOUR FORTHCOMING MARRIAGE, AMY. WE SHALL BE SORRY TO LOSE YOU, BUT OFFER OUR CONGRATULATIONS. YOUR FRIEND, NELLIE, SHALL BE GIVEN THE DAY OFF TO ATTEND.
AMY! YOU'RE MARRYING THAT NICE SAM WALKER—AND YOU NEVER TOLD ME!
AND I'M INVITED TO THE WEDDING!
NELLIE!

THERE IS NO REASON FOR YOU NEGLECTING YOUR WORK, NELLIE.
NO, MA'AM! SORRY, MA'AM!

Nellie was up early on the morning of the wedding.
A WHOLE DAY OFF, AND A WEDDING TO GO TO! OOH, LOVELY!

Dressed in her best, Nellie hurried round to the house of Amy's parents.
YOU ASKED ME TO COME EARLY, AMY.
I'M GLAD YOU'RE HERE, NELLIE. WILL YOU HELP ME GET READY?
MAKE MY HAIR PRETTY, WILL YOU, NELLIE?
YOU LEAVE IT TO ME, AMY. SAM WILL BE PROUD OF YOU.
Amy was ready at last.
THANK YOU, NELLIE. WILL I DO?
YOU LOOK LOVELY, AMY, BUT THE CAB SHOULD BE HERE BY NOW TO TAKE YOU TO THE CHURCH. I'LL GO AND SEE WHERE IT IS!

Nellie ran back after the cab.

Back at the house afterwards, Nellie joined Amy's mother in the kitchen.
IT'S A LOVELY PARTY, BUT THE GUESTS ARE EATING ME OUT OF HOUSE AND HOME!
DON'T WORRY, I'LL HELP YOU!

ANY MORE SANDWICHES, NELLIE?
COMING!
HOW ABOUT A CUP OF TEA, NELLIE?

THEY'RE HAVING A LOVELY TIME. I'LL DO THE WASHING UP AND LET THEM ENJOY THEMSELVES.

Later...
WAKE UP, NELLIE! ALL THE GUESTS HAVE GONE!
IT MUST HAVE BEEN ALL THE EXCITEMENT! WHAT A LOVELY DAY'S HOLIDAY I'VE HAD!

Naughty
DOTTIE
SORRY, I'VE NO PAPER TO WRAP THE UMBRELLA I'VE REPAIRED FOR YOUR FATHER, DOTTIE. WILL YOU TAKE IT AS IT IS?
YES!
ON GUARD, YOU VILLAIN!
TAKE THAT!
FORE!
WHEE-EE-EE!
CHARGE!
HUH! IT LET ME DOWN—HARD!
AND IT LETS IN RAIN!
I DON'T THINK MUCH OF THAT REPAIR! IT'S USELESS!

THE S.O.S. GIRLS

CHERYL MASON and Barbara Blake, the sixteen-year-old daughters of wealthy industrialists are on holiday from their expensive French boarding school. They decide to spend the time helping people in trouble. Jimmy Ferguson, a reporter on the local newspaper, gives them information. One very stormy day they go to see Jimmy in his office.

As the girls passed the circus.....

Two miles farther on they came to a stream they had to cross, but....

At the circus, Barbara found the girl motor-cyclist and explained what she wanted her to do.

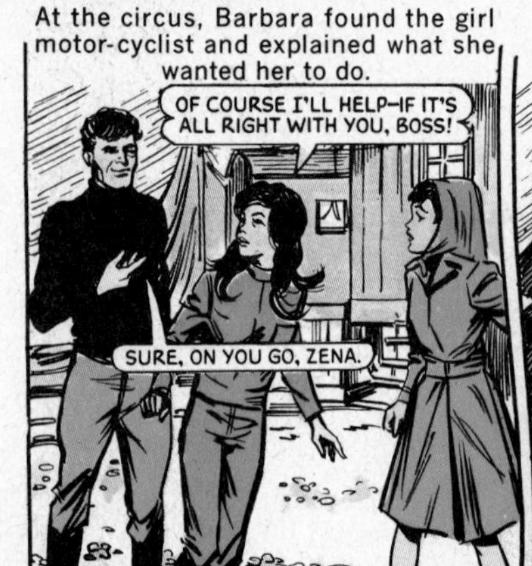

At the broken bridge, the trick motor-cyclist daringly started across the remaining narrow plank.

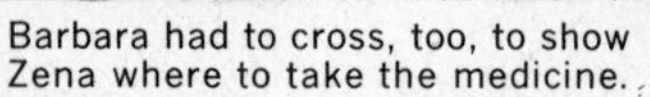

Barbara had to cross, too, to show Zena where to take the medicine.

TOBOGGAN

By teatime there was about a foot of snow on the garden path. Jaqueline went out and shovelled away a short stretch of it, but no sooner was her back turned than it seemed to fill up again.

She began to feel uneasy. Somehow the snow didn't look so pretty as before. And all that evening the wind howled round the cottage like a tribe of whooping Red Indians.

She didn't like sitting alone in the kitchen, and went up to her grandmother's room instead. She had kept a fire burning there all day. But even there she could not quite dismiss her uneasiness whenever the wind let out an especially savage war-whoop.

At half-past nine she could stand it no longer. Her grandmother was dozing. There was nothing to do. She decided to go to bed.

But first she must lock the back door. Opening it an inch or two before she did so, she was aghast to see that the snow was piled up against it now like a huge wave, as high as her chin ! And it was still snowing hard !

Her inside suddenly seemed to go quite cold with fear. Quickly she shut and bolted the door and went to bed.

SNOWED UP!

WHEN Jaqueline woke, only a few snowflakes were drifting past the window, and everything seemed very still. But when she came to look out of the bedroom window, she saw something that took her breath away.

The snow was level with the window-sill !

" It can't be true ! It couldn't snow so much !" she whispered to herself.

But it *was* true ! Running downstairs, she found that all the downstairs rooms were eerily dark, the snow covering the windows entirely, and that the front door and the back door were completely blocked.

They were snowed up !

Jaqueline had always thought this would be very exciting. But now that it had really happened she didn't like it a bit. It was freezing cold all over the house, downstairs especially.

What light got through the snow was so very dim and green that you could imagine yourself miles under the sea. She shuddered, and ran upstairs to tell her grandmother.

Instead of answering, her grandmother moaned, tossed one arm out like a swimmer, and said, " I never was really fond of the sea !"

Her cheeks were all blotchy, and her hand felt terribly hot and dry. She was delirious with fever. Jaqueline knew that people were only like that when they were very ill indeed.

Jaqueline suddenly felt very lonely, very helpless and very young. If only she could fetch a doctor or some other grown-up who would know what was wrong and what to do !

But how could she get a doctor ? She couldn't get out of the house and nobody could get in.

The only hope was that someone in the village would remember them and come and dig them out. But very likely the village was snowed-up, too ! There seemed nothing for it but to grit her teeth and bear it until the snow melted.

All that morning her grandmother went on tossing, and coughing, and groaning, and occasionally saying something quite crazy. She didn't seem to know Jaqueline, or even see her, though her eyes opened at times.

After dinner, Jaqueline could bear it no longer. She went to her own bedroom, sat down on the window-seat and cried.

But presently, feeling a little better, she wiped her eyes and stared out at the snow.

How lovely it had seemed a few days ago—and how cruel, how utterly cruel, it looked now !

Then it had seemed a delightful playfellow. *Now* it was a grim, white-faced gaoler.

Suddenly Jaqueline began to look at the snow more attentively. It was not everywhere as deep as it was against the house. Down at the bottom of the hill, where Lenner Lane ought to be, she could see the top of the hedge poking through the white. Between the house and the lane the snow dipped down in a steady curve.

She remembered that the hedge last summer had been only as high as her shoulders. So the snow there must be only as deep as her shoulders.

But how could that help? It couldn't help to get her out of this house!

A DARING IDEA

AT this point Jaqueline's daring idea came to her. She could use Blue Peter to get her out! If she could ride on the toboggan as far as the lane, where the snow was thinner, surely she could struggle along from there to the village?

But, of course, even in the lane the snow would be awfully deep. No—the idea wouldn't work.

She went back into her grandmother's room. Perhaps her grandmother would be better now and tell her what to do.

"Have you put the cat out, Harry?" her grandmother asked as she went in.

She *must* have a doctor! Well—so be it! Jaqueline would get her a doctor.

Full of excitement, she piled up the fire to last for several hours, put on her green anorak, and wrote a note, saying:

"*Dear Granny,*
I am leaving you for a little while. I shall be back as soon as possible. Don't worry!
Jacky."

This she left on the table by the bedside, together with a fresh cup of water and a clean handkerchief, in case her grandmother should come out of her delirium and be frightened at her absence.

Then she dragged Blue Peter up the steep stairs to her bedroom, opened the smallish window as wide as she could, manœuvred the sledge on to the snow, and tied it by the tow-rope to the window fastener.

She then wriggled through and lay face downwards on Blue Peter, looking for a moment or two down the steep slope of glittering white with a mixture of terror and elation.

It was the steepest run she had yet faced.

But the surface was freezing, and seemed firm enough. So, at length, she took a deep breath and twisted herself round to cut the rope with her penknife.

Whoosh! Away shot Blue Peter—like a canoe over a waterfall!

Jaqueline shut her eyes. The first second had made her feel sick, like that first second on the Scenic Railway. But then the curve flattened, and she was able to open her eyes and to try to brake and steer a bit with her toes.

There was a terrifying bump halfway down, over a three-foot step of snow. She nearly overturned, but, with a frantic wriggle, she managed to keep the toboggan under her. Then came a swerve, just in the nick of time, round a humped white thing—which she knew was once a holly tree.

After that, her speed slowed so much that she was now afraid, not of crashing, but of coming to a stop too soon. She let her legs down and began to urge Blue Peter along. The snow was very soft here, and it was very hard to keep going.

But she managed it. A few minutes after shooting from the bedroom window she was sitting safely grounded on the hedge-tops of Lenner Lane.

" Less than a quarter of a mile now !" she told herself.

The question was, how best to do it? She had meant to walk along from here. But now, perched on her platform of twigs, she found she didn't much like the idea of leaving Blue Peter. Even though the snow was less than the depth of the hedge, it would certainly be well above her waist. There might be deeper drifts in places.

The longer she looked, the less she liked the prospect of trying to walk. It would be more like wading—in stuff much harder than water. Yet to toboggan along the lane was impossible, too. It was practically level all the way.

Then her second idea came to her. Why not use Blue Peter as a sort of snow-punt?

A large straight branch in the hedge nearby offered itself as a punt pole. She leaned over and hacked at it with her knife, and, at last, though tough and obstinate, it was hers.

Then followed the tricky business of getting Blue Peter down into the snow of the lane. The brambles clutched hard, both at her and Blue Peter. But at length, scratched and dishevelled, she was down.

Now for Lenner !

It was gruelling work and painfully slow. There was so little to push against. The pole kept sticking. Sometimes she hardly seemed to be moving at all.

By the time she had done half the distance, she was nearly in tears. Her hands were bleeding, her arms felt red-hot, her head ached, and her clothes were sticky with sweat.

But she had to go on—even when the stick broke, leaving her with a stump of less than a foot long. She couldn't stay there in the middle of the lane, and she was still afraid to get off the toboggan into the snow.

And so, jerkily, slowly as a barge, but not nearly so dignified, her chariot drew at last into the village street, where she could dismount—for the villagers had roughly cleared it of snow.

But how weary she was ! Her legs were like grass stalks under her, and trembling like flames, so that she thought she must be ill. They were still trembling when she knocked at the doctor's door.

He opened it himself. And, at the sight of her, his pipe fell out of his mouth.

" How have *you* got here ?" he demanded.

Jaqueline gave a tremulous smile.

" I *had* to. Granny's very ill. But I couldn't have done it without Blue Peter !" she said, and burst into tears.

. . . . .

Three hours later, when a gang of villagers had cleared a path up to the cottage , when the doctor had given the sick woman some tablets that cooled her fever and sent her to sleep, and the District Nurse had been installed for the night, Jaqueline went to look at Blue Peter.

Only a few bramble scratches were there to prove his latest exploit.

But then, that was all Jaqueline had to prove hers !

ME AND MY FAMILY
HI, there! It's me again—Sandy Shore! Me and my family live in the village of Marston Priors. There's me, and the twins, Chris and Tina; Penny, our little sister; and loads of animals—as well as Dad and Mum, editor of the local newspaper. It was all because of Mum that I got mixed up in my latest adventure—when, believe it or not, I met a Talking Scarecrow! Here's how it all happened . . .

I was passing the village inn with my friend, Helen Bates, on our way home from school. Usually there's nobody near the inn at that time, and we could hardly believe our eyes . . .
WE KNOW HE'S COME TO THIS VILLAGE—HE'S BOUND TO STAY HERE, GIRLS!
TAKE MY AUTOGRAPH BOOK TO HIM!
AND MINE!
GOSH—WHAT'S GOING ON, HELEN?

WHAT'S UP, MRS CRANE?
THESE GIRLS THINK THE POP SINGER, OWEN NAIRN, IS STAYING AT MY INN, BUT HE ISN'T. SEEMS HE'S STAYING SOMEWHERE LOCALLY—RENTED SOME BIG HOUSE, PROBABLY.
WHEE! LET'S GET A MAP OF THE DISTRICT AND GO AROUND ALL THE BIG HOUSES TILL WE FIND OWEN, KIDS!

When I arrived home, I told Mum about the scene in the village.
POOR MRS CRANE JUST COULDN'T CONVINCE THEM OWEN NAIRN WASN'T HIDDEN AWAY AT THE INN.
OWEN NAIRN? AN EXCLUSIVE INTERVIEW WITH HIM WOULD BE A REAL "SCOOP" FOR THE PAPER! SANDY, IF YOU CAN TRACK HIM DOWN AND GET HIM TO AGREE TO SEE ME, I'LL BUY YOU THOSE NEW TARTAN TREWS YOU WANTED!

Naturally, I took up Mum's challenge! Right at the start I got a lucky break, as I was giving Ginger Hackett a hand with the milk crates.
DON'T FORGET THE NEW ORDER—FIVE PINTS A DAY FOR PRIORY HALL, GINGER.
OK, MRS FLETCHER.
PRIORY HALL—THAT COULD BE WHERE OWEN NAIRN IS STAYING. IT'S BEEN EMPTY FOR MONTHS, AND IT'S A LONELY PLACE!

As soon as I could I cycled over to Priory Hall.
WHAT'S THIS? A FOLDER OF BOOK-MATCHES WITH "TONI'S PLACE, BROADWAY" ON THE COVER—AND OWEN NAIRN'S JUST BACK FROM A NEW YORK TOUR. MY HUNCH WAS RIGHT. I'LL JUST SLIP INTO THE GROUNDS WHILE EVERYTHING'S QUIET.

But, a moment later . . .
FUNNY! I COULD SWEAR I'M BEING WATCHED!

WOW! A TRAP!
CAUGHT YOU!

MR NAIRN'S HERE FOR PEACE AND QUIET, ON DOCTOR'S ORDERS, AND FANS ARE GOING TO BE KEPT OUT!
THERE'S THE HOUSE, GIRLS—UP THERE!

No sooner had the keeper let me go than I was grabbed again—this time by the fans!
THIS KID'S JUST BEEN IN THERE! DID YOU SEE OWEN?
LET ME GO!
I had a hard job getting rid of the fans—till I got my hands on some ammunition!
GO AWAY AND LEAVE ME ALONE! I HAVEN'T SEEN OWEN NAIRN AND, WHAT'S MORE, I THINK HE'S A ROTTEN SINGER, ANYWAY!
OUCH! AW—SHE'S CRAZY! LET'S GET BACK TO PRIORY HALL AND WATCH FOR OWEN!
I sat down to have a rest. It was then I got the shock of my life!
SO OWEN NAIRN'S A ROTTEN SINGER, IS HE?
THE S-S-S-SCARECROW! IT SPOKE!
Then, to add to my alarm, the scarecrow came to life!
SORRY IF I STARTLED YOU, BUT I WAS GETTING PRETTY STIFF PUTTING ON MY SCARECROW ACT!
OWEN NAIRN! BUT WHAT ARE YOU DOING DRESSED UP LIKE THAT?

It turned out he had been setting off for a ramble when he'd seen his fans.
I GRABBED THE CLOTHES OFF THE SCARECROW AND TOOK ITS PLACE. THOSE GIRLS WOULD TEAR ME TO PIECES IF THEY CAUGHT ME! BUT HOW AM I GOING TO GET THE BENEFIT OF BEING IN THE COUNTRY WHEN I HAVE TO STAY COOPED UP IN THE HOUSE ALL THE TIME?
H'M...NOW LET'S THINK FOR A MINUTE!
Just then, Ginger Hackett drove along the road below us on his way to deliver milk at Priory Hall, and that gave me a super idea.
GINGER HACKETT—OF COURSE, THAT'S IT! OWEN, YOU'RE GOING TO BECOME A MILKMAN! YOU'LL GIVE MY MUM AN EXCLUSIVE INTERVIEW FOR HER PAPER, WON'T YOU, IF I TELL YOU MY SCHEME?
I'LL GIVE HER ANYTHING YOU LIKE, IF IT LETS ME HAVE A HOLIDAY IN PEACE!

I did a bit of quick shopping in town at a theatrical stores and, next day, when Ginger drove up to the Hall, I was with him.
IT'S THAT KID AGAIN—SHE'S ON THE MILKVAN THIS TIME.
SO FAR, SO GOOD!
WHY DIDN'T WE THINK OF THAT?

Up at the house, Owen and Ginger swopped places—with the help of a couple of wigs!
THE WIG'S FINE, OWEN. I'LL JUST ADD A FEW FRECKLES AND YOUR FANS WILL NEVER RECOGNISE YOU!
I ONLY HOPE THEY DON'T GET HOLD OF GINGER, THAT'S ALL!
DON'T WORRY—MY HOBBY'S LONG-DISTANCE RUNNING!

It all worked like a charm—the waiting fans didn't take a scrap of notice of the real Owen Nairn as he drove under their noses!
LOOK—THERE HE IS!
HE'S SLIPPING OUT BY THE SIDE GATE! QUICK, LET'S CUT HIM OFF!

So Owen Nairn got a peaceful holiday, Mum got her special interview, Ginger got loads of running practice and a hefty tip from Owen's agent for all his help. What did I get? My tartan trews, of course!
OH, WHAT A BEAUTIFUL MORN—ING!
THANK YOU, GINGER. YOU KNOW, YOU'VE GOT A NICE VOICE—MUCH BETTER THAN A LOT OF THOSE SILLY POP STARS!

COLLEEN AND THE LAST WITCH
BUMBLE is the last witch in all Ireland. She is always causing trouble in Ballyvale, where she lives in her new council house—obtained by witchcraft, of course!
Colleen O'Day, the seventh daughter of a seventh daughter, is immune to Bumble's spells and tries to keep her in order.
COLLEEN
At the butcher's van one day....
I'M SORRY—I'VE ONLY GOT ONE CHOP LEFT.
WHAT'S THAT? NO RUMP, T-BONE OR FILLET? IF MY CAT ATE WHAT'S THERE, IT WOULD CERTAINLY KILL IT! I'M NOT A ONE TO MOAN OR TO GRIPE— BUT I'M CERTAINLY NOT GOING TO EAT THAT TRIPE!
MY DAYS OF HAVING NO CHOICE ARE PAST! I'M TIRED OF VANS THAT REACH ME LAST! SO, IN FUTURE ALL VANS WILL BE CURSED INTO BRINGING THEIR GOODIES TO MY HOUSE FIRST!
Later....
MY SPELL IS WORKING, AND EVERY VAN HAS COME ACCORDING TO MY PLAN. AND NOW I'VE COME OFF BEST OF ALL, WITH EVERY VAN AT MY BECK AND CALL!
When the fish van came....
THIS ISN'T FAIR—IT WAS THE TURN OF THAT END OF THE STREET TO BE SERVED FIRST TODAY, MR O'REILLY.
THIS OLD COD IS OUT OF PLACE! 'PON MY SOUL, I'LL BRING TEARS TO HER FACE!
YOUR SUPPER WILL BE EMPTY PLATES— YOUR HADDOCK'S JUST PUT ON ITS SKATES!
MY FISH! OH, WHAT'LL MY HUSBAND SAY WHEN HE COMES HOME TO CHIPS AND NOTHING ELSE?
But soon word of what was happening got to Colleen.
EVERYBODY'S COMPLAINING BECAUSE BUMBLE GETS SERVED FIRST BY EVERY VAN THAT COMES INTO THE ESTATE.
EVERY VAN? WELL, I THINK WE CAN SOON SHAKE HER!
MR MURPHY? COLLEEN O'DAY HERE. WOULD YOU DO ME A FAVOUR? I KNOW YOU'RE TAKING YOUR VAN OUT TOMORROW, SO WOULD YOU TAKE IT TO MULLIGATAWNY ESTATE FIRST?
Next morning, Mr Murphy's van stopped outside Bumble's door.
TV DETECTOR
IT'S THE TV DETECTORS!
THANK GOODNESS THEY WENT TO BUMBLE'S FIRST!

TV had only recently come to Ballyvale, so few had licences. There was great scurrying around as people hid their sets.
TV DETECTOR
THERE THEY GO. 'TIS A SHAME 'TIS ONLY THE FIRST ONE IN EACH PLACE IS EVER CAUGHT.
HEH—HEH! BUMBLE WON'T BE GLAD THAT VAN CALLED FIRST AT HER HOUSE!
Bumble had to stump up for her TV licence, and no sooner had Mr Murphy left than another van called.
I'M FROM THE SOCIETY FOR THE PREVENTION OF CRUELTY TO IRISH CATS. I HOPE YOU KNOW THAT, IN THIS AREA, ALTHOUGH DOGS NEED NOT BE LICENCED, CATS MUST?
WHAT'S THAT? A LICENCE FOR MY CAT? FIRST TIME I'VE EVER HEARD OF THAT!
YOU MUST PAY ME ONE POUND FOR EACH CAT OR KITTEN.
I THINK I REALLY HAVE BEEN BITTEN! ONE POUND FOR EVERY CAT OR KITTEN! THAT MEANS A TOTAL OF FIVE PAY-UPS! THAT CAT! WHY DIDN'T IT HAVE PUPS?
HO-HO! STUNG AGAIN, BUMBLE!
HEE—HEE! HERE'S THE NEXT ONE— AND HER CHIMNEY IS SMOKING NICELY!
S.P.C.I.C.
SORRY, BUMBLE—IGNORANCE IS NO DEFENCE. THIS IS A SMOKELESS ZONE. THAT'LL BE A FIVE POUND FINE
I SHOULD HAVE REALISED BEFORE— THIS IS COLLEEN'S WORK ONCE MORE! I'M NOT SO RICH AND I'M NOT SO DUMB— I'LL TAKE THE VANS JUST WHEN THEY COME!
I'VE HAD MY FILL OF BEING FIRST! THAT SPELL HAS MADE ME COME OFF WORST! VANS AND LORRIES GO AWAY; DON'T COME HERE FIRST ANOTHER DAY!
GOOD! THAT FIXED HER!
Half an hour later, Colleen was passing Bumble's house again, when ....
SPLUTTER! RAGE! JUMP AND KICK! THIS BUSINESS MAKES ME REALLY SICK!
WHAT'S UP NOW?
THE SOAPO SUDS MAN IS HERE GIVING AWAY FIVERS— AND HE'S GONE TO SOME-ONE ELSE FIRST!

JANIE B. QUICK

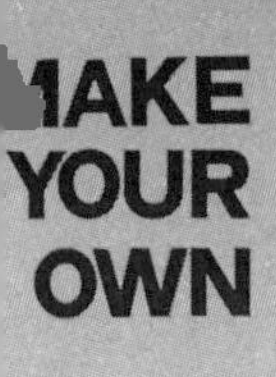

MAKE YOUR OWN 3-D VIEWER

WHAT do you do with all the picture post-cards you are sent—throw them away? Don't — you can make a super viewer with them. You will need a paper-tissue box, or a shoe-box, about 5 in. wide and 8 in. long; a small mirror; scissors; sticky tape and, of course, as many picture postcards as you can find.

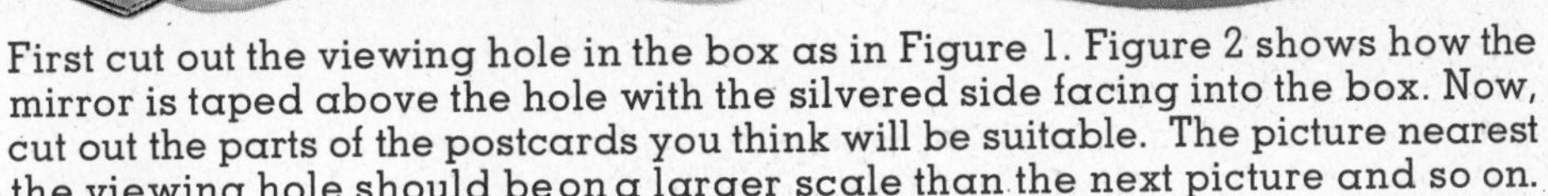

First cut out the viewing hole in the box as in Figure 1. Figure 2 shows how the mirror is taped above the hole with the silvered side facing into the box. Now, cut out the parts of the postcards you think will be suitable. The picture nearest the viewing hole should be on a larger scale than the next picture and so on.

Figure 3 shows how to trim off sky and other parts that are not needed. The last picture you use should be a complete card, supplying the background.

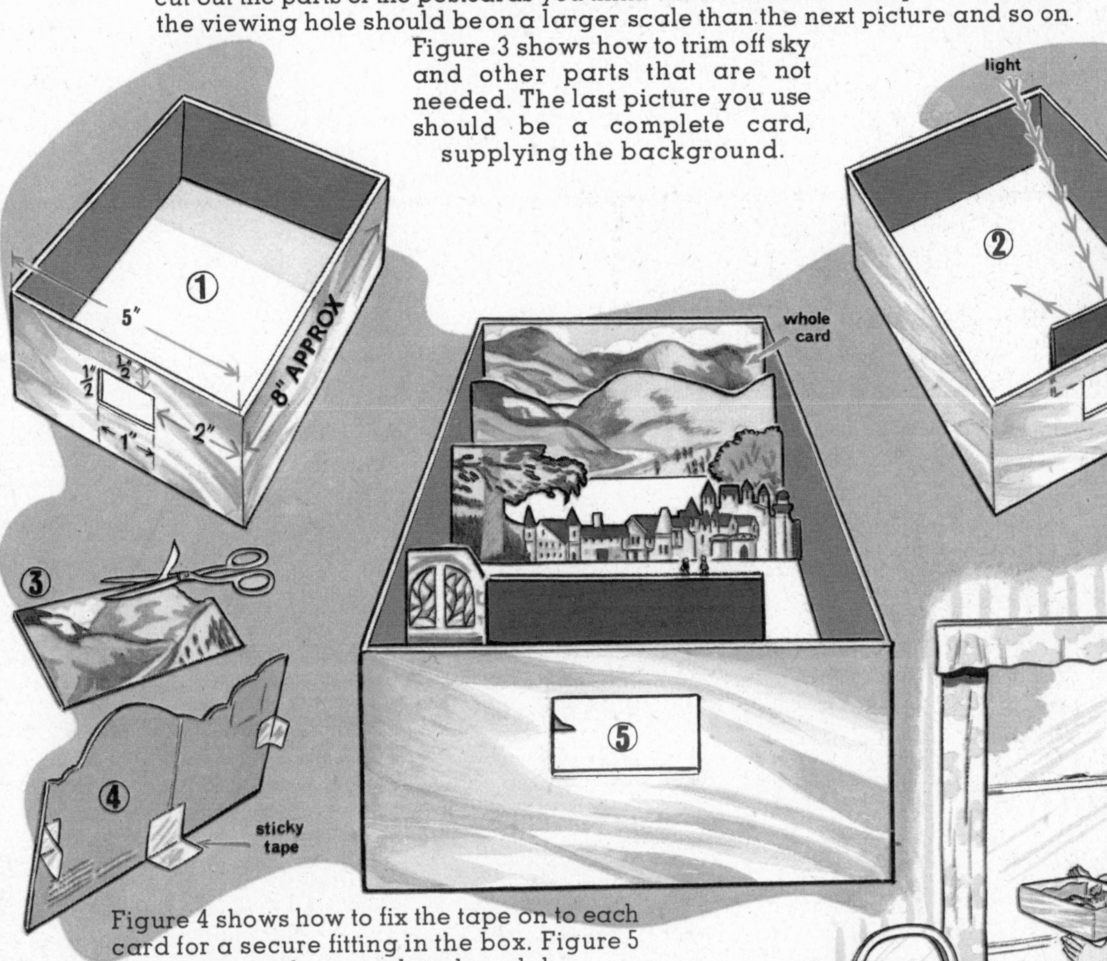

Figure 4 shows how to fix the tape on to each card for a secure fitting in the box. Figure 5 shows the completed model.

Now, hold your viewer up to the window, or to a light. The light reflected by the mirror helps to separate the different sections and gives your model a three-dimensional effect.

DOGS' HOMES!
EACH of the five dogs on the right side of the page is connected with one of the countries below. Do you know the dogs' homes?
a
This dog is used in Greenland to haul sledges and can withstand extreme cold.
In Wales it was originally a cattle dog, but is now a popular pet the world over.
b
Many travellers in the Swiss Alps owe their lives to this enormous dog.
c
Although this dog is popularly called French, it is German in origin and was used as a sheep herder and waterfowl dog.
CAFÉ FRANÇAISE
ECOLE
d
One of the world's smallest dogs, bred in Mexico.
e
1 ST. BERNARD.
2 POODLE.
3 CHIHUAHUA.
4 HUSKY.
5 CORGI.
ANSWERS 1-c, 2-d, 3-e, 4-a, 5-b.

PEGGY PORKER

You can make Peggy easily with an egg box, some impact glue and poster paint. A useful tool for cutting the pieces from the egg box is a craft knife. Below you can see the egg box. You will need only the lid. Cut along the broken lines and you have the two halves which make Peggy's body.

CUT OFF AT BROKEN LINE.

CUT ALONG BROKEN LINES TO MAKE FEET.

CUT ALONG BROKEN LINES FOR THE HEAD.

Now cut half of one of the middle sections out as shown. This will make the head. Next cut the top off the peak in the middle of the lid. Cut this into quarters and you have the legs. The next thing to do is to glue together the first two pieces you cut out. You now have the body.

On the right you can see where to glue the head and feet. The tail can be cut from any curved part of the lid. Glue the head on first, then the four legs. This will enable you to balance the model when you glue on the legs.

The last touch is to paint Peggy with poster paint. You can paint flowers, or any other design, on Peggy.

THE STRANGE STORY OF MILLIE MOLD

THERE was one sure and certain fact about Miss Millie Mold—she would never win a Miss World title! Come to that, she'd never even be Miss Toddlepuddle, where she lived. She'd never be anything, thought Millie.

She did pause and wonder at the noise, but it didn't seem to mean very much . . .
FLY-FLY-FLY-S-S-S-SAUCE--!
SPA-SPA-SPA-PEEP-PEEP-PEEP-PEEP-PEEP!
So Millie maintained her miserable march, looking neither to left nor right—and not seeing that live people had been turned into purple statues!
MUST HAVE BEEN A FIRE, OR SOMETHING!

Frozen in action by purple paralysing rays, they didn't get a second glance from Millie. And, little did she know it, but the little space people were just around the corner, ready to turn their ray-guns on her!

Suddenly they came face to face!
AH-ER-EM-UM-HMM!
CAN IT BE.... DO I SEE ?
THE SAME AS ME? IT MUST BE SHE!
Imagine Millie's surprise when the Green Men, who were purplising everybody a minute earlier, threw themselves down on the ground before her.
WHO, ME?
SHE!

In a trice, the whole invasion force was there, space ships forgotten, ray-guns abandoned. And all they could do was chant in adoring unison....
SHE!
SHE!
SHE!
SHE!

Nothing like this had ever happened to Millie before, so she did the most natural thing in the world—she ran like the wind!
COME BACK, GREAT PINK QUEEN!

She won the race home by a short pair of spectacles, slammed the door behind her and, gasping for breath, listened to the chanting from the Green Men.
IT IS THE PROPHECY OF OUR FOREFATHERS— "ONE DAY YOU WILL FIND A GREAT PINK QUEEN".
EH? MUST BE NUTS!

Millie's mum had left the TV set switched on for the news.
THE INVASION BY SPACE ALIENS SEEMS TO HAVE STOPPED. REPORTS SAY THEY ARE SEARCHING FOR A GREAT PINK QUEEN!

Millie, putting two and two together, thought . . .
IF THEY WANT A QUEEN...
... THEY CAN HAVE ONE!

Fired with patriotic fervour, Millie stepped before the assembled green horde and spoke . . .
OK! I'LL BE YOUR QUEEN!

Millie very soon developed a liking for her regal role and issued orders with abandon.
UNPARALYSE THOSE PEOPLE!
THIS CHAIR IS MOST UNCOMFORTABLE! THRONE TOGETHER, IT WAS!

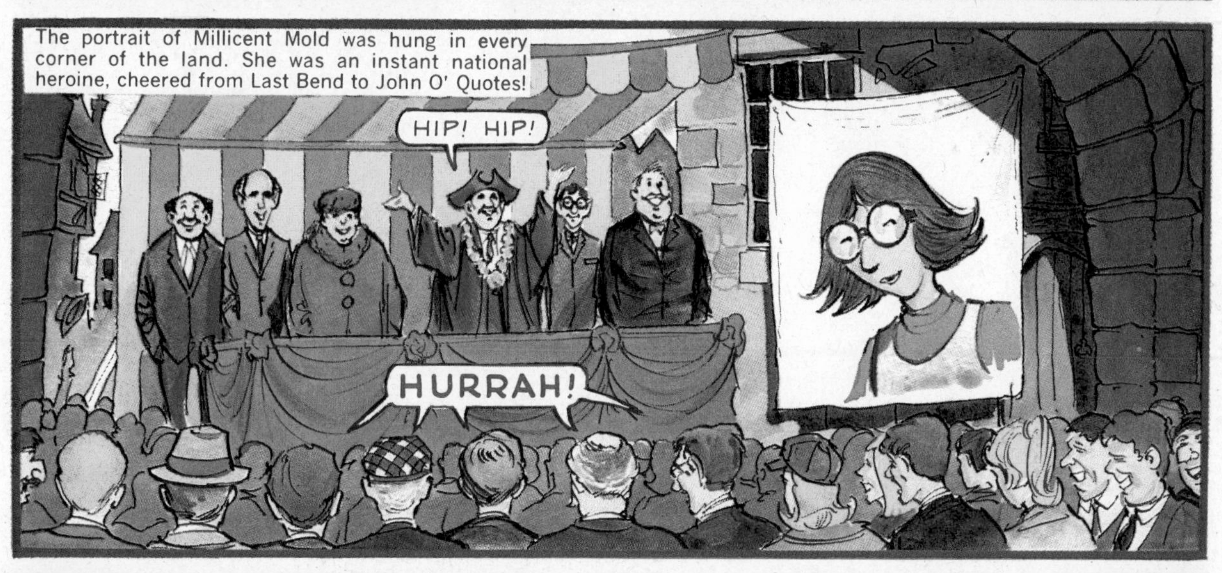
The portrait of Millicent Mold was hung in every corner of the land. She was an instant national heroine, cheered from Last Bend to John O' Quotes!
HIP! HIP!
HURRAH!

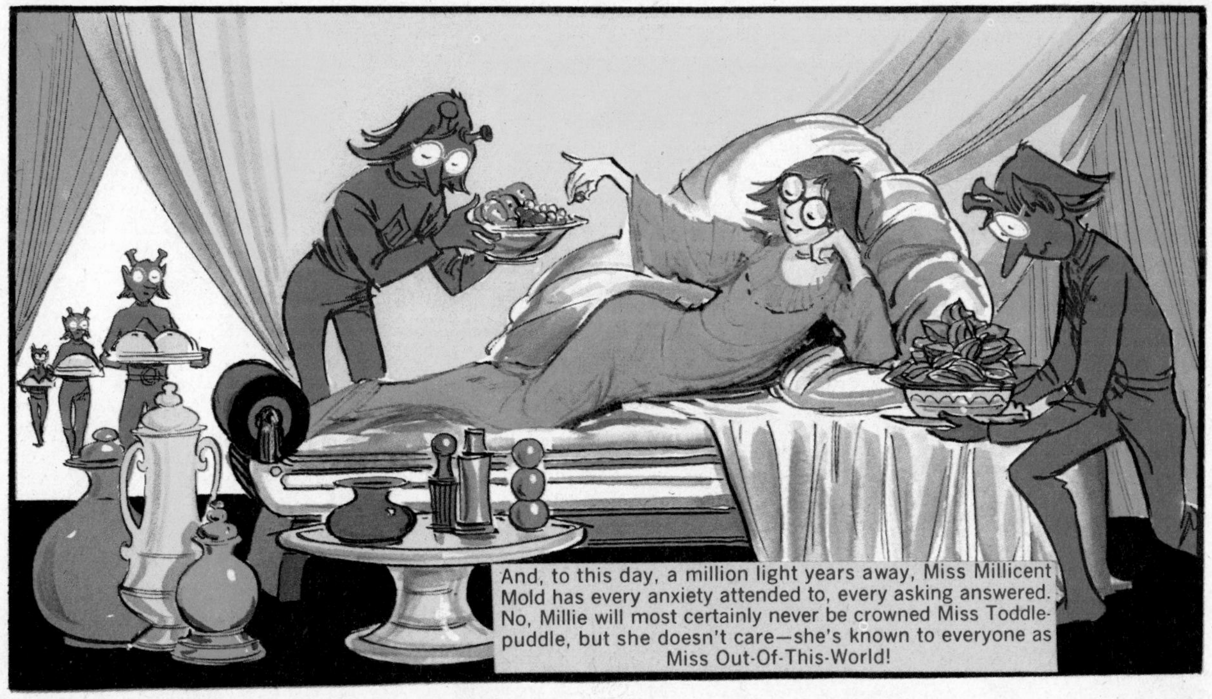
And, to this day, a million light years away, Miss Millicent Mold has every anxiety attended to, every asking answered. No, Millie will most certainly never be crowned Miss Toddle-puddle, but she doesn't care—she's known to everyone as Miss Out-Of-This-World!

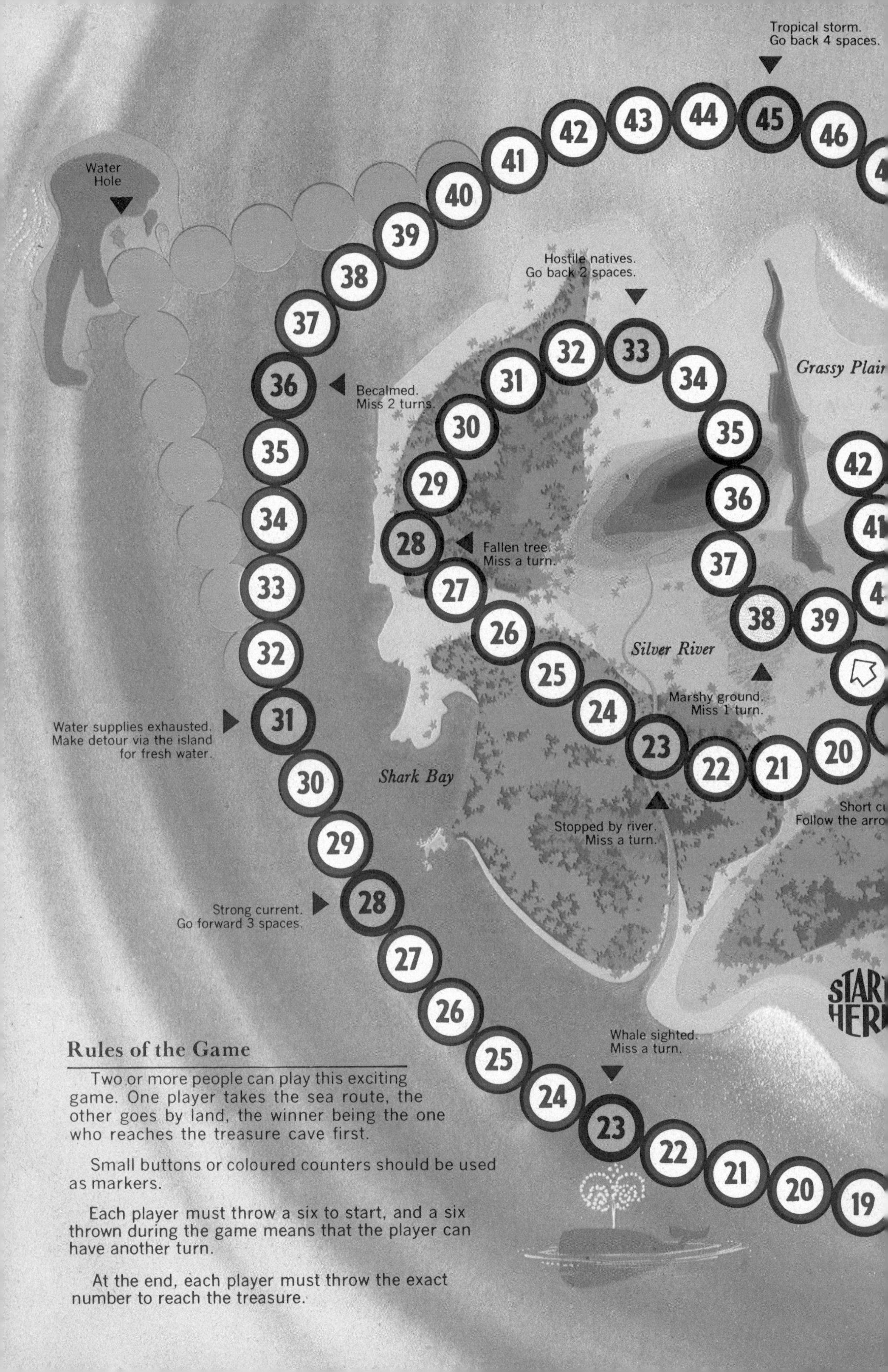

Rules of the Game

Two or more people can play this exciting game. One player takes the sea route, the other goes by land, the winner being the one who reaches the treasure cave first.

Small buttons or coloured counters should be used as markers.

Each player must throw a six to start, and a six thrown during the game means that the player can have another turn.

At the end, each player must throw the exact number to reach the treasure.

THE PEARLS OF POONA

This is Poona Island. Hidden in a cave is a chest of pearls. The hunt for it will give you and your friends lots of fun.

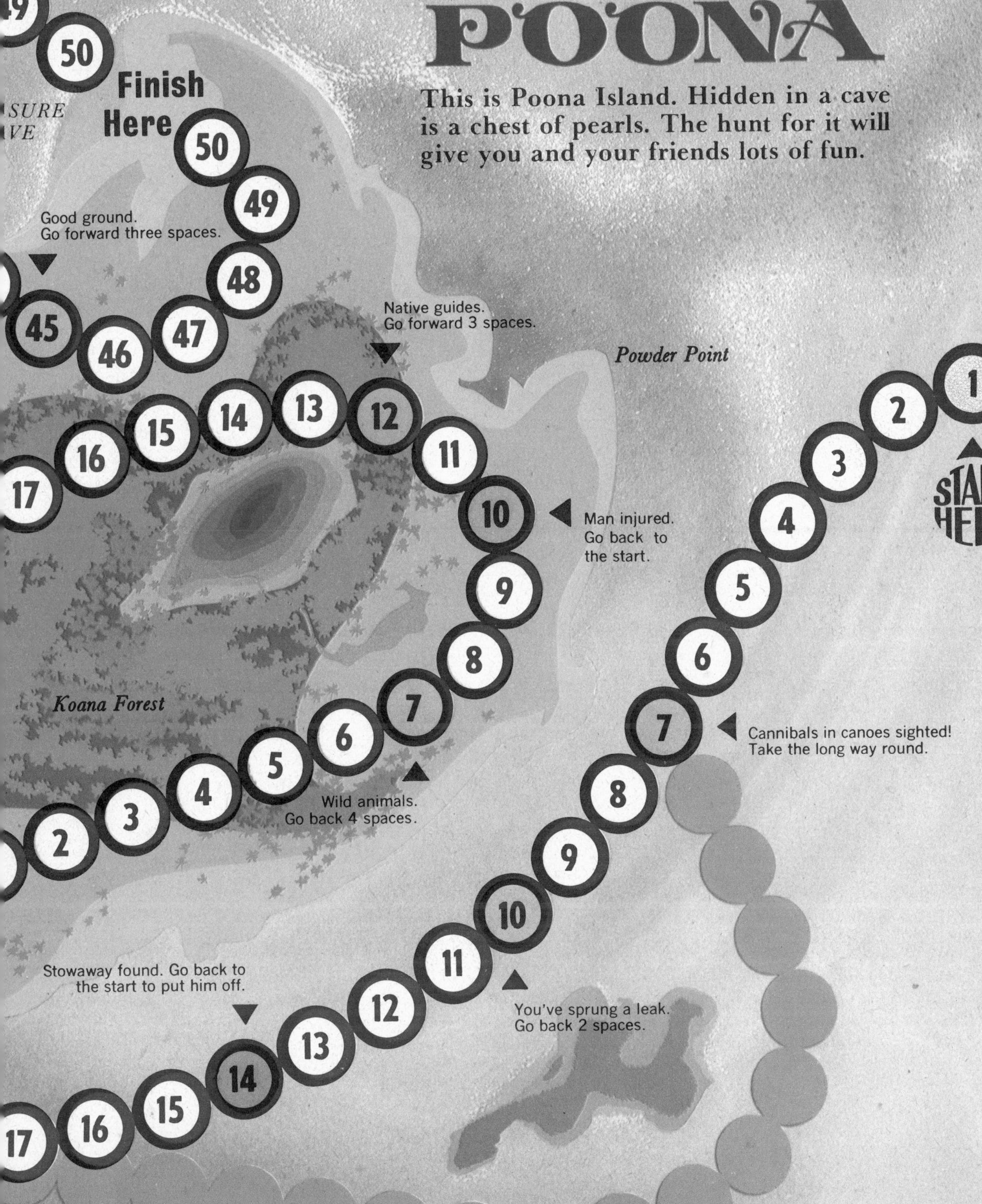

POP PLAQUES

WHY not make a super wall plaque to decorate your room? On the right you see Carole all set to make one, with her materials ready. You will need 1 lb. of plaster of paris from your chemist, or cellulose filler from a handyman's shop. The other necessities are a mixing bowl, spoon, a flat piece of wood like a ruler, and a plate or saucer big enough to take the picture you want to use for your plaque.

Lightly grease one inch all round edge of plate. Let's say you want to make a plaque of your favourite pop star. Cut the picture from a magazine and place the photo face down on the plate. Mark the edge of plate with a piece of sticky paper to show where the top of the plaque will be when it is finished.

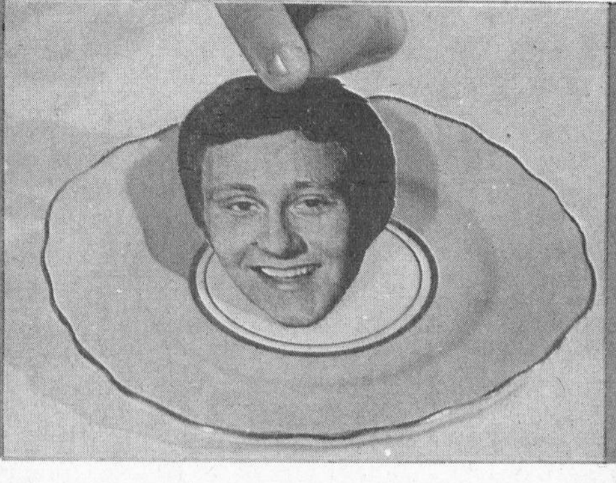

Put as much plaster in the bowl as will more than fill the plate level with the edge. Pour in water slowly until the plaster absorbs it. Let it stand for half a minute then stir until plaster is smooth and without lumps.

Working very quickly, stir the mixture into a fine paste. The plaster will get hard and unworkable in about five minutes.

Holding the picture in position in the centre of the plate, quickly put in a spoonful of plaster on to the picture and hold it in position.

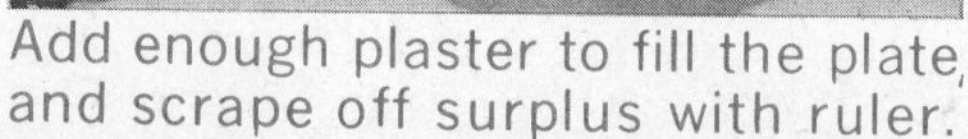
Add enough plaster to fill the plate, and scrape off surplus with ruler.

Twist a piece of wire or string as shown in the diagram and place over the position marked at the top of the job. This makes sure that plaque won't hang upside down! Cover the wire with a spoonful of plaster and smooth it out. When dry, this makes the loop for hanging your plaque on the wall. Another way is to make a hole with a match before the plaster hardens.

Leave for a few hours to let the plaster set, then gently tap the back of the plate and your plaque will fall out quite cleanly.

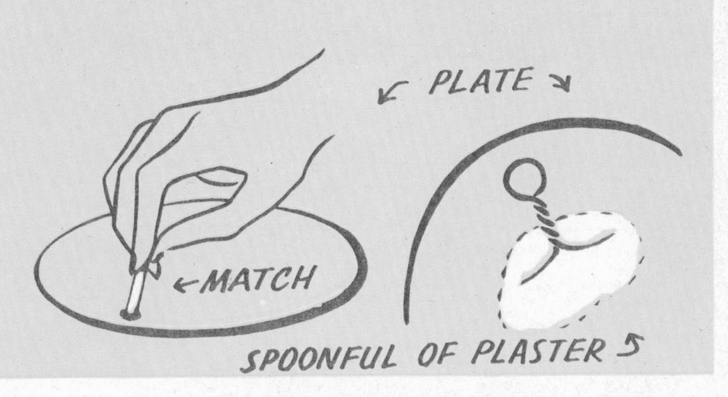

Cover the table with several layers of paper. Wear an apron, for plaster will stick to your clothes. Sandpaper can be used to even any rough edges. Work as quicky as possible with the plaster and follow the mixing instructions. Wash up all dishes and spoons immediately—and don't use the Sunday crockery, just in case!

If you feel that the plaques do not fit in with the colour scheme of your room, there are many ways in which you can brighten them up. Paint the edges, bind coloured tape around the edges, use small transfers or stick-on designs to vary the frames. There are endless possibilities for making them more attractive.

DOUBLE DANGER
DURING the school holidays, Fiona McGregor applies for a job as companion-help to Mrs Maxwell-Hope. There are many older applicants and she is a little surprised when she is chosen by Mr Maxwell-Hope for the job.
SHE LOOKS EXACTLY RIGHT.

Later, approaching Maxwell Manor . . .
GOOD EVENING, MISS FIONA.
HOW DID HE KNOW MY NAME?
OH, NEWS TRAVELS FAST IN THESE PARTS, MY DEAR.

Fiona had little to do that evening and went to bed early. During the night, she suddenly sat up drowsily.
WHAT'S THAT I HEARD?

AAAAAAH!
Fiona's scream brought Mrs Maxwell-Hope to the room.

I SAW SOMEONE WHO LOOKED EXACTLY LIKE ME OVER THERE!
IT WAS ALL IN YOUR IMAGINATION, MY DEAR. LOOK—IT'S A MIRROR THERE. YOU MUST HAVE SEEN YOUR OWN REFLECTION.

Next morning, it certainly all seemed like a bad dream.
MY WIFE SUGGESTED YOU MIGHT LIKE TO TRY SKINDIVING FOR FRESHWATER MUSSELS. WE HAVE ONE OF THE BEST PEARLING RIVERS IN SCOTLAND RUNNING THROUGH OUR GROUNDS.
I'D LOVE THAT!
So, a little later . . .

KEEP WELL AWAY FROM THE BLACK SPOUT, FIONA. IF YOU WERE SWEPT INTO THAT UNDERGROUND RIVER... OH, HELLO, JAMIE.
'MORNING, SIR; 'MORNING, MISS FIONA. YOU DON'T NEED ANYONE TO TELL YOU ABOUT THE DANGERS OF THE BLACK SPOUT, SEEING WHAT HAPPENED TO...

Mr Maxwell-Hope interrupted before the gardener could complete what he was saying and Fiona felt uneasy, but she soon forgot it in the thrill of gathering pearl-mussels underwater.
Fiona and Mr Maxwell-Hope collected over one hundred mussels—and Fiona was lucky!
OH, LOOK AT THIS! I'VE FOUND A PEARL—AND IT'S A BEAUTY!

I'LL GO IN AGAIN AND SEE IF I CAN GET SOME MORE MUSSELS, THEN...

AAAAH!

Strong swimmer though she was, Fiona was swept into the Black Spout.
THAT TAKES CARE OF YOU!

LIGHT—THERE MAY BE A WAY OUT THIS WAY! I CAN'T SWIM BACK AGAINST THE CURRENT!

Her lungs bursting, Fiona swam desperately through the side tunnel and suddenly emerged in a cave.
PHEW! THANK GOODNESS!

THERE'S A PASSAGE IN THERE!

The girl in the secret room explained that she was Fiona Maxwell, whose parents had recently died. If she herself died, the estate went to her cousins, the Maxwell-Hopes. Reluctant to spill family blood, the Maxwell-Hopes had formed a plan of bringing in, as companion-help, a girl who looked like the heiress and killing her instead, so that it would be thought that Fiona Maxwell had died in an accident. The heiress would then have been kept a permanent prisoner. The mirror in Fiona McGregor's room actually covered the door into the secret compartment in which Fiona Maxwell had been held captive.

The girls' story was believed at once, for the gardener had sent for the police himself. His suspicions, already aroused, had been increased when his employer stopped him talking to Fiona earlier at the riverside about the local man who had recently been drowned in the Black Spout.

PHOTO FUN

HUH! I'D RATHER BE IN THE DOG HOUSE THAN LOOK LIKE A DOG'S DINNER!

WHAT DO THEY EXPECT **ME** TO DO- GET IN THERE WITH HIM?

DOG

THIS BRITISH CLIMATE- GIVE ME THE ANTARCTIC ANY DAY!

OW! GET OFF MY FOOT!

Lorna's Leprechaun
LORNA DONOVAN, who lives in the little Irish town of Ballybog, is an ordinary schoolgirl except for one thing—a leprechaun called Murphy has come to stay with her. Murphy can imitate anything he chooses, and then only Lorna can see him as he really is.
One day Lorna and Murphy were sunbathing in the garden.
DAD'S ENJOYING HIMSELF, ANYWAY, MURPHY!
AND SO AM I, TO BE SURE! THIS IS THE LIFE OF REILLY!
Just then, Mr Donovan made a wild swing.
THAT WAS A BAD SHOT! OH, OH! HERE COMES MR SQUASHMAN, THE LOCAL BRAGGART.
HO! HO! CALL YOURSELF A GOLFER, DONOVAN? I SAW THAT!
I COULD PROBABLY GIVE YOU A START AND BEAT YOU!
IS THAT SO? I CHALLENGE YOU TO EIGHTEEN HOLES TOMORROW!
DAD DOESN'T HAVE A CHANCE, MURPHY. MR SQUASHMAN IS A GOOD GOLFER.
SURE AND I'LL HAVE TO DO SOMETHING ABOUT THAT, LORNA! YOU OFFER TO CADDY FOR YOUR FATHER TOMORROW.
So, next morning at the first hole...
NOW'S MY CHANCE, LORNA! IT'S A GOLF TEE I'LL BE!
Only Lorna could see Murphy.
Murphy took the place of Mr Squashman's tee.
WATCH ME DRIVE, AND YOU'LL PICK UP SOME TIPS, MR DONOVAN.
But...
WOW!
THAT'S A GOOD EXAMPLE OF A BAD GOLF STROKE, MR SQUASHMAN!

Murphy allowed the first hole to be played, but after both men had driven off at the second...
THERE'S MR SQUASHMAN'S BALL, LORNA! BEGORRAH I'LL MAKE A GOOD IMITATION!

So when Mr Squashman finally noticed his ball—it was Murphy.
HEY!
Murphy led Mr Squashman a merry dance before, finally...
M...MY GOLF BALL! IT'S DISAPPEARING DOWN THAT RABBIT HOLE.

But when Mr Squashman put his hand in after it...
AH! A RABBIT!
Mr Squashman thought Murphy was a real rabbit.
The bemused Mr Squashman summoned Lorna and her father.
LOOK! MY GOLF BALL CHANGED INTO THIS RABBIT!
As soon as Mr Squashman spoke, Murphy changed his shape again.
IT DOESN'T LOOK LIKE A RABBIT TO ME.
WH...WHAT? IT-IT'S A GOLF BALL AGAIN!
MURPHY REALLY HAS HIM WORRIED.

Mr Squashman put down the ball and tried to appear nonchalant.
JUST MY LITTLE JOKE, DONOVAN. NO HARD FEELINGS, EH? I'LL PLAY MY SHOT NOW.
I WONDER WHAT MURPHY'S NEXT MOVE WILL BE!

Mr Squashman reached for one of his clubs.
GOOD FOR MURPHY!
I...IT CAN'T BE!

WHAT'S WRONG NOW?
MY...MY CLUB'S TURNED INTO A HOCKEY STICK.

IT LOOKS LIKE AN ORDINARY CLUB TO ME!
I...IT CAN'T BE! I...I DON'T THINK I'M VERY WELL! R...RABBITS! HOCKEY STICKS. I...I CONCEDE THE M...MATCH, DONOVAN! I'M G...GOING HOME!

WELL I THINK YOU'VE TAUGHT MR SQUASHMAN NOT TO BRAG, MURPHY!
BEGORRAH! LOOK AT HIM RUN! LOOK! HE'S GONE A FAIR WAY ALREADY!

Sandra's Shadow
I MUST FIND OUT WHO SHE IS.
FOR several mornings Sandra Wilson, star of the Edmund Lawrence Ballet Company, has noticed a little girl outside, copying her every move.
When Sandra went to the door . . .
STOP! COME BACK!
Although the girl would not stop, Sandra was convinced she would return next day, and made plans accordingly . . .

Next day . .
AH! THERE'S THE LITTLE GIRL AGAIN—AND SHE THINKS JOYCE IS ME!
WALK TOWARDS THE DOOR IN A COUPLE OF MINUTES, JOYCE. BY THAT TIME I'LL BE OUTSIDE, READY TO FOLLOW THE GIRL WHEN SHE RUNS.

Later . . .
MY TRICK WORKED. THE GIRL DOESN'T KNOW I'M FOLLOWING HER.

THAT MUST BE WHERE SHE LIVES.

Sandra went to the door.
I'M SANDRA WILSON, A BALLET DANCER. I'M MAKING ENQUIRIES ABOUT A LITTLE GIRL WHO SEEMS TO BE VERY KEEN ON DANCING.
WHY, THAT MUST BE MY DAUGHTER, JANE.

But, when Jane was asked to dance . . .
THAT'S STRANGE. HER DANCING ISN'T NEARLY SO GOOD.

I HOPE YOU'LL GIVE HER AN AUDITION, MISS WILSON.
ER...WE'LL SEE.

But, as Sandra left the house . . .
PLEASE DON'T GO ON WITH THIS, MISS WILSON! IT WILL ONLY LEAD TO TROUBLE!
BUT...

The woman, Mrs Taylor, told Sandra that she was housekeeper to Mrs Jones. The little dancer copying Sandra's movements was Sue, Mrs Jones's stepdaughter. Mrs Jones was determined that her own daughter would be a ballet dancer, even if it meant that her stepdaughter was robbed of her chance. Unfortunately, Sue's father was abroad working for an oil firm.

SOMEONE OUGHT TO TELL MR JONES WHAT'S GOING ON. THE HOUSEKEEPER GAVE ME THE NAME OF THE COMPANY HE WORKS FOR. PERHAPS I CAN FIND OUT SOMETHING FROM THEM.

Sandra went to the public library to find out the address of the company.
SILENCE
HMM! THE MANAGING DIRECTOR OF THE COMPANY IS SIR NEVILLE O'BRIAN, A KEEN BALLET FAN. I WONDER..

Sandra went to see Sir Neville.
THANK YOU FOR GIVING ME SO MUCH OF YOUR VALUABLE TIME, SIR NEVILLE.
A PLEASURE, MY DEAR. AND DON'T WORRY ABOUT THAT LITTLE MATTER. IT WILL BE TAKEN CARE OF.
Sandra'phoned Mrs Jones.

WE SHOULD LIKE YOU TO BRING YOUR DAUGHTER TO ANOTHER AUDITION, PLEASE.
CERTAINLY, MISS WILSON!

Later, at the airport . . .
B.O.A.C
THAT'LL BE THE 'PLANE BRINGING MR JONES HOME.

A few minutes later . . .
NO EN
MR JONES? I'M SANDRA WILSON. I KNOW YOU'RE A BIT BEWILDERED, BUT I'LL EXPLAIN THINGS TO YOU ON THE WAY TO THE BALLET AUDITION.

At the audition . . .
I HOPE I'M DOING THE RIGHT THING!
THANK YOU, JANE.

NOW WE HAVE ANOTHER LITTLE GIRL FOR AN AUDITION, MRS JONES.

MY STEP-DAUGHTER! WHAT'S GOING ON HERE?

Sue danced superbly.
BRAVO!

SUE SHOULD BE GIVEN THE CHANCE TO BE PROPERLY TRAINED.
UNLESS MY OWN DAUGHTER GETS THE SAME CHANCE, SUE CERTAINLY SHAN'T!

WE'LL SEE ABOUT THAT!
JOHN!

MY FIRM'S TRANSFERRED ME HOME. I'LL BE WORKING IN ENGLAND FROM NOW ON— AND THERE WILL BE SOME CHANGES MADE IN OUR HOUSEHOLD!

Some weeks later . . .
WHY, HELLO!
YOU'LL BE GLAD TO KNOW WE'RE ALL MUCH HAPPIER NOW. SUE'S GETTING ON WELL WITH BALLET; JANE HAS TAKEN UP HORSE-RIDING.

I'M GLAD THINGS WORKED OUT ALL RIGHT FOR MY LITTLE SHADOW!

ANNIE'S ARK

ORPHAN Annie Bright is in charge of Chipper's Circus menagerie, the animals from which are hired out to do acting jobs.

THAT'S RIGHT. ROSIE LOVES BEING HOSED. GOSH! WE'RE BOTH SOAKING!

WHO CARES? I'M HAVING A SUPER TIME, ANNIE! LOOK AT BEPPO—HE WON'T LEAVE ME!

JUNIOR NANNY
ISN'T SHE LOVELY?
LIKE A LITTLE FAIRY.
I WISH THE WOMEN WOULDN'T FUSS OVER HER SO.
CHRIS WARREN is training at a residential nursery for the under-fives. One little girl, Sylvia, is very pretty and the compliments she gets are making her conceited.

That evening . . .
COME ON, SYLVIA; INTO BED.
I SUPPOSE I AM VERY PRETTY.

DON'T BE SO ROUGH, NURSE CHRIS! FAIRIES BREAK VERY EASILY!
BED, I SAID. PEOPLE WON'T LIKE YOU IF YOU BOAST ABOUT YOURSELF.

Next day, Chris found girls handing over their sweet ration to Sylvia.
WHAT'S GOING ON?
THEY WANT ME TO HAVE THEM, NURSE.
WE DON'T MIND GOING WITHOUT.

Eventually, Chris got the truth out of them.
SHE SAID SHE'D TURN YOU INTO TOADS? NONSENSE! SYLVIA IS JUST AN ORDINARY LITTLE GIRL, SAME AS YOU ARE.
I'M NOT! I'M A LITTLE FAIRY. THE LADIES SAY SO, AND FAIRIES CAN DO SPELLS.

That afternoon . . .
WHAT ARE YOU DOING IN YOUR PARTY DRESS? IT'S JERSEYS AND JEANS FOR THE PARK.
NOT FOR FAIRY QUEENS LIKE ME. WE HAVE TO WEAR PRETTY DRESSES ALL THE TIME.

I WANT MY DRESS ON!
FOR A FAIRY YOU'VE A VERY LOUD VOICE! KEEP STILL AND BEHAVE!

At the park . . .
WOULD YOU LIKE ME TO SIT UP BY YOU AND TELL YOU ABOUT FAIRYLAND?
OH, THE LITTLE DEAR!
OH, THE LITTLE MADAM! STILL, PERHAPS SHE'LL HAVE A TANTRUM WHEN I TAKE HER AWAY—AND THEN THEY WON'T DOTE ON HER SO MUCH.

But Sylvia behaved sweetly.
'BYE-'BYE. SEE YOU TOMORROW.
SUCH LOVELY MANNERS!
LITTLE DO THEY KNOW!

At tea time . . .
NO, SYLVIA. YOU'VE HAD TWO CAKES ALREADY. YOU'LL BE SICK!
I WON'T. I'M NEVER SICK.
THAT'S TRUE. SHE HAS A HUGE APPETITE...AH!

At breakfast next day . . .
A SPECIAL TABLE ALL FOR MY OWN! OOH, IT IS PRETTY.
FIT FOR A FAIRY QUEEN!

But when Chris set the table . . .
WH-WHAT'S THIS?
YOUR BREAKFAST, FAIRY-SIZED. EVERYONE KNOWS THAT FAIRIES ARE VERY SMALL AND ONLY EAT TINY MEALS.

I WANT A PROPER BREAKFAST. I WANT...
...TO BE A LITTLE FAIRY. YOU'VE TOLD US. STEADY, OR YOU'LL SPILL YOUR MILK.
A fairy-sized dinner and tea were also set and Sylvia began to cry.
I'M HUNGRY! I WANT SOME MORE, PLEASE, NURSE!
WELL, NOW, IS IT SYLVIA MATHEWS ASKING—OR QUEEN SYLVIA?
SYLVIA MATHEWS, NURSE. THAT FAIRY QUEEN HAS GONE AWAY! IT'S ME!
THAT'S GOOD. I WASN'T KEEN ON HER. RIGHT! A GIRL-SIZED TEA IT IS.

There was no more preening for her.
WHAT HAS COME OVER THAT DEAR CHILD? SHE'S SO NOISY NOW.
NOT A BIT CAREFUL OF HER APPEARANCE. SHE'S CHANGED!
IN OTHER WORDS, SHE'S JUST A NORMAL GIRL AGAIN!

Dottie,

How about you filling up this page? Write something you think the readers might be interested in.

The Editor.

Dear Readers

its all very well for him (the editor) but i don't know what to rite about. I is not very good at English but i think my spelling is gud don't you??

What do I say oooh, blotch! i went to the dog show I meet my friend doris who was showing her dog and her dad – but they didn't win anything. When i went outside it was reigning cats and dogs – there were poodles on the road – HA, HA! Joke. Ha, HA! I thought that was funny HE! He! seriously, tho, i did not have wet shoes on so i took a bus home – well, the bus took me home. a bus

Then my sister who had just finished electrocution classes YEOH ELECTRO CUTION in Paris (france) – for her own good – came to our house. She is wet. She was brides made at a wedding we all throo sphagettii at her. She wasn't ooh another blot? pleased cos mine was still in the packet and hit her in the eye At night i watch t.v. witch works by eccentricity My mother says I'll get square eys from watching it (me with square eys) but i didn't get them from reading comics – you don't have square eys do you?!

A while ago i went to the museums and i saw mummies in boxes with ejipshens ~~hire byrogt~~ riting on it Horrible it was. looked just like my mummy Oh, oh! mummy oh dear this pen has just come in and is reading over my shoulder splutter she's making funny spluttering sounds and her hand looks as if it's going to come down on me

Polly and her Pram
Polly often helps Mum by taking Baby out.
GOO!
I DON'T LIKE THE LOOK OF THIS SALESMAN.
YOUR MOTHER NOT IN? WELL, PERHAPS...
I DON'T WANT TO BUY ANYTHING, THANK YOU.
HOW ABOUT ONE OF OUR TOP-QUALITY UNBREAKABLE COMBS?
GOO!
GOLLY! THAT'S BROKEN YOUR UNBREAKABLE COMB!
AHEM! THEN SUPPOSE WE TRY A PRAM COVER INSTEAD? THESE ARE GUARANTEED MOTHPROOF, STAINPROOF AND CREASE-RESISTANT.
BUT IT ISN'T BABYPROOF!
R-R-R-RIP!
WELL, HOW ABOUT...
MY TIE'S CAUGHT! WOW!
THE LOCK'S SNAPPED SHUT! I CAN'T GET IT OPEN!
YOU MEAN IT'S AN OPEN AND SHUT CASE!
THE LOCK'S JAMMED! YOU JUST WAIT TILL I GET THIS TIE FREE!
HERE COMES A POLICEMAN. LET'S DISCUSS IT WITH HIM!
I'VE NEVER SEEN A TRAVELLING SALESMAN TRAVEL SO FAST!
GOO!

The TALKING ROCK
CALENDAR
14 DEC
DON'T WORRY...
...THE TALKING ROCK WILL HELP YOU!
THE Talking Rock, in a cave in Appledore, is connected to young Tabby Cooper's grandmother's cottage by a rock channel through which sound travels. By means of the channel, an old woman who once lived in the cottage secretly gave help and advice to people who told their troubles to the Talking Rock, and Tabby decides to carry on her good work.
Sally Drew and her elder sister, Dinah, had bought long-vacant Appledore Manor and turned it into a hotel. One day Tabby called at the Manor.
HELLO, TABBY! GOOD NEWS! THE HOTEL'S FULLY BOOKED FOR THE CHRISTMAS HOLIDAYS! THE FIRST GUESTS ARRIVE TODAY!
APPLEDORE MANOR HOTEL
THAT'S GREAT! I'LL GIVE YOU A HAND WITH THE DECORATIONS, SALLY!
Dinah seemed nervous about the preparations.
PLEASE TRY TO LOOK LESS LIKE A TRAMP WHEN MY SPECIAL FRIENDS ARRIVE, SALLY!
OK, DINAH!
GOLLY! LOOK AT THAT SUPER CAR THAT'S DRAWING UP!

DINAH'S POSH FRIENDS! COME ON, TABBY! WE'LL GO TO THE OFFICE AND CHOOSE THE GAMES FOR OUR CHRISTMAS-EVE PARTY. THAT'LL SAVE DINAH HAVING TO INTRODUCE ME AS HER GRUBBY LITTLE SISTER!

Half an hour later . . .
WE'LL HAVE MUSICAL BUMPS AND CHARADES...
WHAT AN UTTER BORE!

COLETTE'S RIGHT! NO CORNY OLD GAMES! OUR GUESTS WILL WANT ORIGINAL, CLEVER ENTERTAINMENT AND COLETTE'S KINDLY OFFERED TO ORGANISE IT!
DINAH! TABBY AND I SPENT AGES ON THAT LIST!
DINAH'S FINE FRIENDS SEEM TO BE TAKING OVER! OH! MORE GUESTS ARRIVING. I'D BETTER BRING IN THEIR LUGGAGE.
DON'T LET THINGS GET YOU DOWN, SALLY. LET ME KNOW IF YOU NEED ANY MORE HELP.
A few evenings later, Tabby was busy dressmaking in the cottage kitchen.
CALENDAR
23 DEC
IT WAS NICE OF DINAH AND SALLY TO SEND ME A PARTY INVITATION...OH! I CAN HEAR SOMEONE IN THE OLD CAVE!
The opening in the rock channel was hidden by the kitchen calendar.
IT'S SALLY'S VOICE!
I HEARD THE LEGEND ABOUT YOU HELPING PEOPLE, TALKING ROCK. I'M WORRIED ABOUT MY SISTER'S NEW FRIENDS. DINAH HAS GIVEN THEM FREE ROOMS IN THE HOTEL AND LENT THEM MONEY. THEY'RE JUST TAKING ADVANTAGE OF HER KIND NATURE!
As the voice of the rock, Tabby answered that all would be well.
COLETTE AND HER FRIENDS SOUND LIKE EXPERT CADGERS! POOR SALLY!
The next day, Christmas Eve, Tabby was helping with last-minute jobs before the party.
DINAH, DARLING! THAT SILLY LITTLE CHRISTMAS TREE IS A FRIGHTFUL DRAG! ALL THAT STUFF WENT OUT WITH THE BUSTLE!
COLETTE GOES TO ALL THE BEST SOCIETY PARTIES, SALLY. SHE'S SURE TO KNOW BEST. PUT THAT TREE OUT OF SIGHT ON THE UPSTAIRS LANDING!
YOU'RE LETTING YOUR FRIENDS RUN OUR HOTEL AND...
QUIET, SALLY! THEY'RE GOING TO RECOMMEND OUR HOTEL TO ALL THEIR RICH FRIENDS AND RELATIVES, SO I'M ONLY TOO GLAD TO DO THEM A GOOD TURN IN EXCHANGE!
HUH! IF THEY HAVE SO MANY WEALTHY RELATIVES, WHY ARE THEY SO SHORT OF CASH?

Not long after, when Tabby set off home . . .
THAT'S ODD! COLETTE AND HER FRIENDS ARE GOING DOWN A DEAD–END ROAD. IT MIGHT BE WORTHWHILE FINDING OUT WHAT THEY'RE UP TO.

Tabby easily followed the car tracks in the snow.
THIS IS THE ONLY SAFE PLACE TO TALK. LET'S GET THE PLAN STRAIGHT.
WHILE YOU SING, COLETTE, AND I PLAY THE PIANO, NIGEL CAN BE GETTING AWAY WITH THE PUSSIES!
THEY'RE PLOTTING SOMETHING— BUT WHAT'S THIS ABOUT PUSSIES? NIGEL DOESN'T STRIKE ME AS A CAT–LOVER. I'D BETTER STAY AND SEE WHAT ELSE I CAN FIND OUT!

The next evening, Tabby arrived early for the party.
HELLO, TABBY! COLETTE'S ENTERTAINMENT IS NEXT. LET'S HOPE THE GUESTS ENJOY IT!
THEY CERTAINLY DON'T LOOK VERY HAPPY AT THE MOMENT!

Colette's singing did nothing to make the guests any happier!
WE WON'T STAY HERE AGAIN! THE FOOD'S GOOD, BUT THE PLACE IS DEADLY DULL!
IT'LL BRIGHTEN UP ANY MINUTE NOW! I SEE THAT NIGEL'S MISSING. I THINK IT'S TIME I MOVED THE CHRISTMAS TREE!

Tabby wasn't away long and, back with the guests, she waited for Nigel to come dashing around the blind corner at the top of the stairs. Suddenly . . .
MY TRAP'S WORKED! IT'S A PITY THOSE "PUSSIES" DON'T SCRATCH!
AAAAAH!
THAT'S MY FUR COAT!
AND THAT LOOKS LIKE MINE! THE THIEF!
Caught red-handed, Nigel at once dragged in his accomplices.
YOU BUNGLING FOOL!
YOU CROOKS! TO THINK I BELIEVED IN YOU AND ADMIRED YOU! YOU PLANNED EVERYTHING IN ORDER TO STEAL FROM MY GUESTS!
After the crooks had been taken away by the police . . .
I ALWAYS KNEW THEY WERE A BAD LOT, TABBY! THE TREE ISN'T DAMAGED AT ALL. WE'LL BRING IT DOWN. WASN'T IT STRANGE THAT IT WAS STANDING IN THE MIDDLE OF THE STAIRWAY?
THAT ISN'T THE ONLY STRANGE THING. I-I ASKED THE TALKING ROCK TO UNMASK DINAH'S SO-CALLED FRIENDS-AND IT'S HAPPENED! DO YOU BELIEVE THAT THE TALKING ROCK CAN REALLY HELP PEOPLE, TABBY?
WE MUST ALL BELIEVE IN A LITTLE MAGIC AT THIS TIME OF THE YEAR, SALLY!
Later, there was a real party at the Appledore Manor Hotel.
HA! HA! A GOOD OLD-FASHIONED PARTY! THIS IS MORE LIKE IT!
WE'VE ALREADY BOOKED TO STAY AT THIS HOTEL NEXT YEAR!
DINAH AND SALLY CAN LOOK FORWARD TO A BRIGHT FUTURE, THANKS TO THE TALKING ROCK!

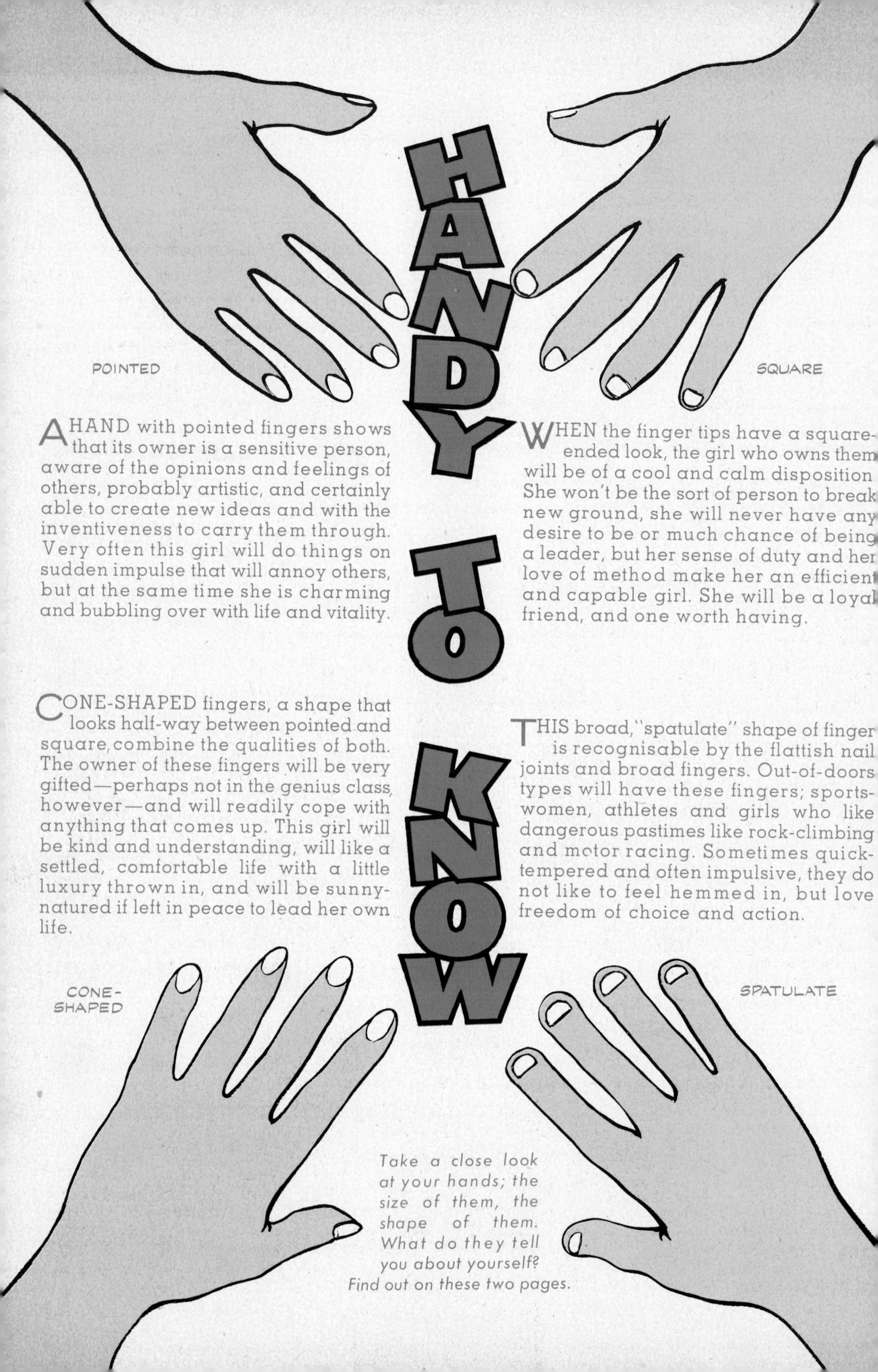

HANDY TO KNOW

A HAND with pointed fingers shows that its owner is a sensitive person, aware of the opinions and feelings of others, probably artistic, and certainly able to create new ideas and with the inventiveness to carry them through. Very often this girl will do things on sudden impulse that will annoy others, but at the same time she is charming and bubbling over with life and vitality.

WHEN the finger tips have a square-ended look, the girl who owns them will be of a cool and calm disposition She won't be the sort of person to break new ground, she will never have any desire to be or much chance of being a leader, but her sense of duty and her love of method make her an efficient and capable girl. She will be a loyal friend, and one worth having.

CONE-SHAPED fingers, a shape that looks half-way between pointed and square, combine the qualities of both. The owner of these fingers will be very gifted—perhaps not in the genius class, however—and will readily cope with anything that comes up. This girl will be kind and understanding, will like a settled, comfortable life with a little luxury thrown in, and will be sunny-natured if left in peace to lead her own life.

THIS broad, "spatulate" shape of finger is recognisable by the flattish nail joints and broad fingers. Out-of-doors types will have these fingers; sportswomen, athletes and girls who like dangerous pastimes like rock-climbing and motor racing. Sometimes quick-tempered and often impulsive, they do not like to feel hemmed in, but love freedom of choice and action.

Take a close look at your hands; the size of them, the shape of them. What do they tell you about yourself? Find out on these two pages.

A long thumb, well past the middle of the first finger joint, is a sign of a strong character, probably a leader, certainly someone very capable and very forceful.

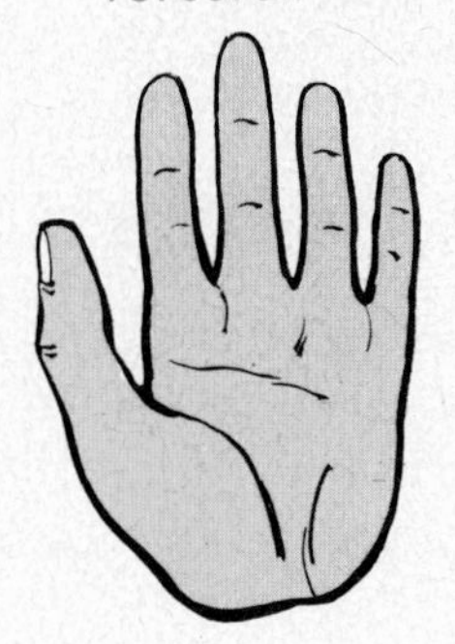

A fairly short thumb shows a gentle personality, someone who pushes herself into the background and is not good at making decisions.

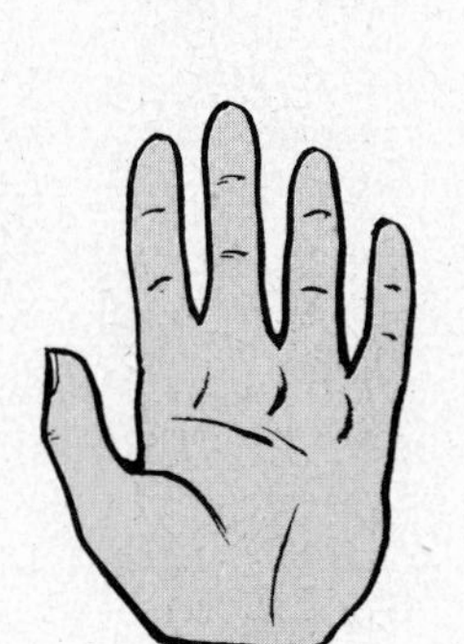

An average thumb shows a contented, tolerant person, willing to see the other person's point of view; willing to be led, but ready to make a stand against injustice.

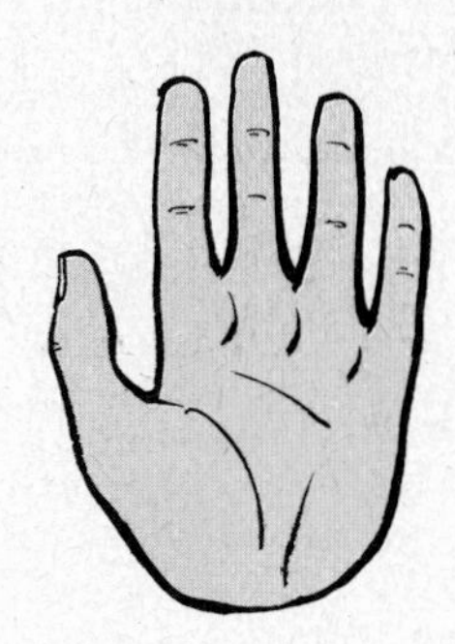

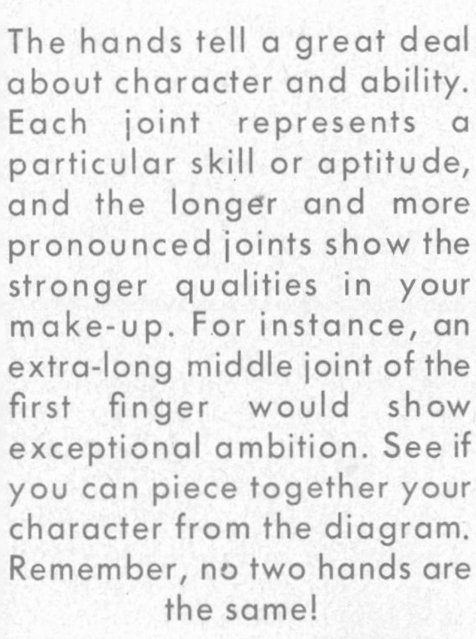

The hands tell a great deal about character and ability. Each joint represents a particular skill or aptitude, and the longer and more pronounced joints show the stronger qualities in your make-up. For instance, an extra-long middle joint of the first finger would show exceptional ambition. See if you can piece together your character from the diagram. Remember, no two hands are the same!

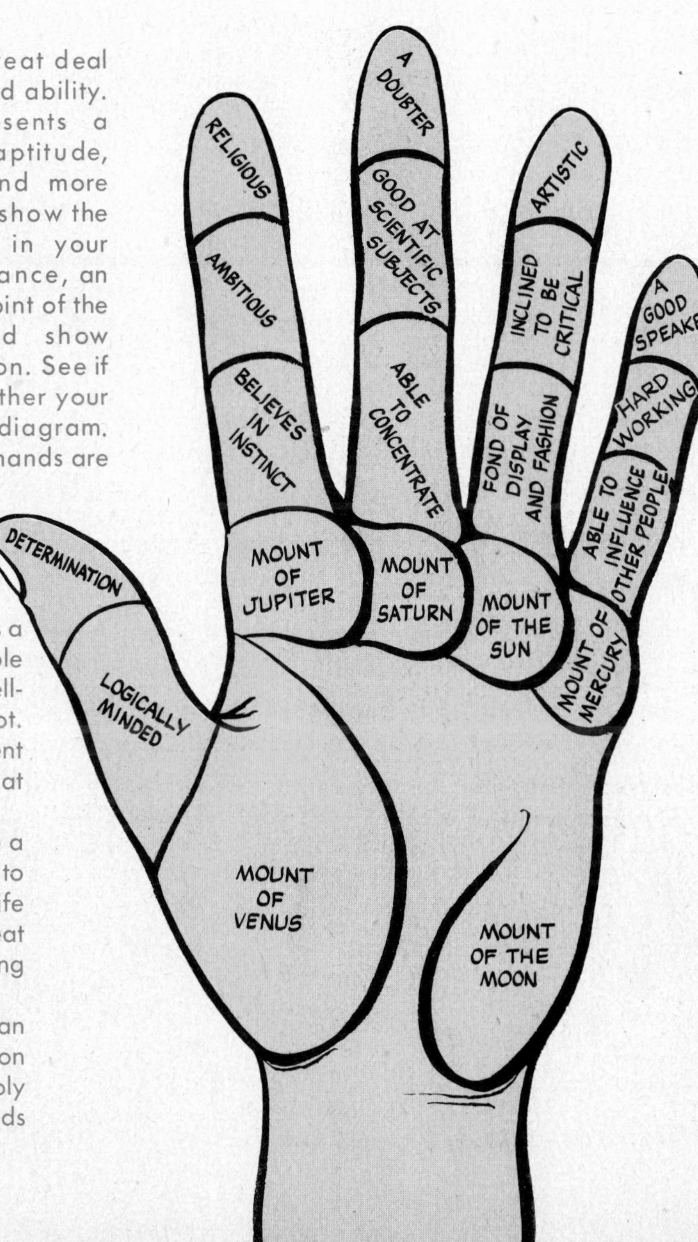

Below each finger is a mount. Some people have these well-developed, others not. If you have prominent ones, here is what they mean:—

VENUS—You are a very easy person to know, full of life and a great capacity for liking other people.

JUPITER—You are an ambitious person and will probably get great rewards out of life.

SATURN—If it is smooth your life will be uneventful, but if there are lines crossing it, look out for excitement!

SUN—Money and glory from this mount. Normal size of mount means you have just enough of these. Cross-lines means you will have to work for them!

MERCURY — Shows your brainpower and business sense —the bigger the mount, the more you've got! Vertical lines on this suggest nursing may well be the vocation for you.

MOON—The larger the mount, the more artistic and poetic the owner will be.

Our Class
HELLO, there! I'm Cherry Bright and, with my two pals, Clem Sanders and Pam Stringer. I'm in Form 1A at Southlands School for Girls. Our gym mistress, Miss Laurel, is also careers mistress, and she took us along to riding stables the other day. Rhoda Weekes, the class show-off, was swanking as usual.
THIS IS MR STANNARD, GIRLS, WHO HAS KINDLY INVITED US TO LOOK ROUND HIS STABLES.
I WOULDN'T MIND WORKING HERE...

Rhoda was only too eager to give us all a demonstration of her riding.
OH, I WISH I COULD RIDE LIKE THAT.
WELL DONE! SHE RIDES BEAUTIFULLY.
WHY DOES SHE HAVE TO SWANK SO MUCH?
Pam was very keen, but she made a mess of trying to mount up.
OH, JUST LOOK AT HER!
BE QUIET, RHODA!

PERHAPS SOME OF YOU WHO HAVEN'T BEEN TOO SUCCESSFUL ON HORSEBACK WOULD LIKE A RIDE IN THIS.
SUPER!
THAT'S MORE LIKE IT, CHERRY!
We thought Miss Laurel would go with us, but . . .
OH, NO!
YOU CAN HANDLE HORSES, RHODA. PERHAPS YOU'D TAKE THE OTHER THREE IN THE TRAP.
CERTAINLY, MISS LAUREL.

Pam was upset by her failure to ride a horse. I thought it might cheer her up if she had a turn with the reins, but Rhoda wouldn't hand over.

We were coming to the Downs, but were too busy to see the notice as we flashed by.
KEEP OUT
ARMY MANOEUVRES
I CAN'T HOLD HIM! I THOUGHT YOU COULD HANDLE HORSES, RHODA?
I CAN'T! I CAN'T!
I DIDN'T KNOW THEY WERE BRINGING IN THE CAVALRY!
KEEP DOWN!
Next moment, we were over the brow of a hill and in the thick of an army exercise!

I don't know what would have happened if one of the soldiers hadn't pulled up our horse.
WHOA!

A sergeant-major strode up angrily.
IT'S A GOOD JOB WE WERE USING DUMMY AMMUNITION OR YOU MIGHT HAVE BEEN KILLED! WHAT'S THE IDEA OF BRINGING THAT PONY AND TRAP HERE?
NOW LOOK WHERE YOUR SWANKING GOT US, RHODA!

One of the soldiers took charge of the pony and trap and we were bundled into a jeep.
THERE'LL HAVE TO BE AN INQUIRY ABOUT THIS. YOU MUST ALL COME TO THE BARRACKS.
WE'RE REALLY FOR IT NOW!

While we were waiting, Mr Stannard and Miss Laurel stormed in.
WHAT IS THE MEANING OF THIS? CAN'T YOU GIRLS BEHAVE YOURSELVES FOR FIVE MINUTES?
I DID WARN THEM NOT TO LEAVE THE FIELD.
WE'RE WAITING FOR THE C.O. TO SEE WHAT TO DO WITH THEM!

The Commanding Officer came in at that moment.
THAT'S THE MAN WHO STARTLED OUR HORSE IN THE FIRST PLACE!
WHAT?
I WAS OUT IN CIVILIAN CLOTHES AS AN OBSERVER.

The Colonel had to admit that he was to blame and invited us all to a super tea.
I DON'T THINK I'D LIKE TO WORK IN THE STABLES AFTER ALL. I THINK I'LL JOIN THE ARMY INSTEAD!

PERSONALITY PAT

PAT TAYLOR ***is a junior sub-editor on "Personality Playmag", a national women's weekly. One morning the editor gives her a pile of photographs.***

With all the votes counted, Pat reported to the editor.

THEY'RE IN ORDER, SIR—THE WINNER'S ON TOP.

THAT'S FINE, PAT. TAKE THE PICTURES TO MR MACMURPHY OF THE ART DEPARTMENT, PLEASE.

Mr Maddock, the chief sub-editor, was with Mr MacMurphy when Pat took the photographs to him.

THIS PHOTOGRAPH HAS BEEN TAMPERED WITH TO MAKE THE CHILD LOOK PRETTIER.

WHAT? LET ME SEE IT.

YES...YOU CAN SEE WHERE IT HAS BEEN PAINTED AROUND THE FACE. WE MUST TELL THE EDITOR ABOUT THIS, BUT HE'S GONE FOR THE REST OF THE DAY. HAVE TO LEAVE IT TILL MORNING.

SURELY NO ONE WOULD DO A THING LIKE THAT!

TWENTY-NINE LANCASTER STREET. LANCASTER STREET...I'M SURE I'VE SEEN THAT SOMEWHERE. AND WHAT'S THE NAME? SENT BY MRS BROWN.
MRS J. BROWN 29 LANCASTER STREET
That evening, as Pat walked home from her bus-stop . . .
I KNEW I'D SEEN THAT NAME—I JUST COULDN'T PLACE IT. I THINK I'LL GO ALONG AND HAVE A LOOK AT NUMBER TWENTY-NINE.
LANCASTER ST.
THAT'S THE BABY—I'M SURE IT IS. BUT SHE'S LOVELY—EVEN BETTER THAN THE PHOTOGRAPH. I WONDER IF I DARE...YES, I WILL!
EXCUSE ME, MRS BROWN, BUT DID YOU SEND A PICTURE OF YOUR BABY TO THE COMPETITION?
YES, I DID—WHY?
WELL ...ER...TO BE FRANK, IT WAS PICKED AS A WINNER, BUT WE FOUND THE PHOTOGRAPH HAD BEEN ALTERED.
OH, DEAR! YOU SEE BABY HAD THE MUMPS WHEN THE PHOTOGRAPH WAS TAKEN AND SO I ALTERED IT TO HIDE THE SWELLING. I'M SORRY.
I QUITE UNDERSTAND, BUT YOUR BABY SHOULD WIN, MRS BROWN. SHE'S BEAUTIFUL.
TELL YOU WHAT—I KNOW SOMEONE WHO'LL TAKE ANOTHER PICTURE VERY QUICKLY. I'LL BE BACK IN HALF AN HOUR.
Next morning, at the office . . .
BRING ME THE PHOTOGRAPH OF THAT BABY, PLEASE!
THIS IS WHERE THE FUN STARTS!
THIS PHOTOGRAPH HASN'T BEEN ALTERED, MADDOCK!
BUT...BUT, I SAW...
POOR OLD MADDOCK—BUT IT WAS THE ONLY WAY! MRS BROWN'S BABY REALLY HAD TO WIN THE FIRST PRIZE.
ALL THAT COUNTS IS THAT HER BABY IS REALLY THE BONNIEST! EVERYONE SAID SO!

MAGNETIC MAGGIE
MAGGIE MURDOCH accidentally receives a powerful electric shock and finds that she becomes magnetic whenever she rubs her chin.
YOU CAN TAKE YOUR OWN TIME WHEN YOU'RE MAGNETIC!
One wet Saturday morning...
WOULD YOU MIND POPPING DOWN TO THE SUPERMARKET FOR ME, MAGGIE?
OK, MUM! BETTER MAKE OUT A LIST. I'VE GOT A MEMORY LIKE A SIEVE!
The heavy rain had caused huge puddles at the level crossing.
OI! WATCH IT!
SERVES YOU RIGHT! YOU SHOULD USE THE PEDESTRIAN BRIDGE!
When Maggie reached the supermarket...
YOU IDIOT! CAN'T YOU USE THE CASH REGISTER PROPERLY?
I'M SORRY, MR BLAGGER. I'VE GOT A BIT OF A HEADACHE THIS MORNING.
SO THAT ROADHOG'S THE NEW MANAGER HERE, IS HE?
BOTHER! I'VE LOST THAT SHOPPING LIST MUM GAVE ME! I'LL JUST HAVE TO TRY TO REMEMBER WHAT WAS ON IT. NOW, WAS IT SPAGHETTI OR BAKED BEANS?
YOU NINCOMPOOP!
Unthinkingly, Maggie had rubbed her chin and, becoming magnetic, attracted one of the food cans.
WHOOPS!
SPICES
DRIED FRUIT
SUGAR
TEA
DON'T YOU KNOW HOW TO STACK GOODS, YOU—OUCH!
ZUNK!
WELL, THAT EVENS THE SCORE—BUT I REALLY MUST BE CAREFUL!
The blow on the head didn't improve the manager's temper and, a few minutes later....
GOT YOU! TRYING TO SNEAK OUT WITHOUT PAYING, EH?
OH! NO, REALLY I WASN'T...
WHY, THAT'S OLD MRS MILLER. SHE'D RATHER STARVE THAN STEAL ANYTHING!

I DIDN'T GET ANY OF MY SHOPPING HERE. YOUR PRICES ARE TOO HIGH!
WE'LL SEE ABOUT THAT! COME TO MY OFFICE! THE BOSS WILL BE HERE SOON!
THAT MANAGER NEEDS TO BE TAUGHT A LESSON! AH, THOSE TROLLEYS! I'LL RUB MY CHIN, AND...
SQUASHES
SOUPS
THIS'LL SHOW THE BOSS I'M ON MY TOES.
I CAN SEE MYSELF GOING PLACES—FAST!
SQUASHES
SOUPS
QUICK! OUT OF THE WAY, MRS MILLER!
WHAAAH!
WHAM!
PICKLES
HELP! STOP THIS THING!
CRASH!
OW!
Then...
THE BOSS!
WHAT'S THE MEANING OF THIS, BLAGGER? I DON'T PAY MY MANAGERS TO ACT THE FOOL! YOU'RE FIRED!
THAT BULLY WON'T BOTHER YOU ANY MORE, MRS MILLER...
LOOK OUT, MY DEAR!
SPECIAL OFFER!
The warning came too late—and Maggie had forgotten she was still magnetic.
SPECIAL OFFER!
MORE OF BLAGGER'S INCOMPETENCE, I SUPPOSE! HE'S HAD THESE BASKETS INCORRECTLY STACKED!
I'M SORRY ABOUT THIS. KINDLY ACCEPT THIS FIVE POUND VOUCHER.
ER—THANK YOU, SIR!
HERE YOU ARE, MRS MILLER. WITH THIS VOUCHER, YOU WON'T HAVE TO WORRY ABOUT THE GOODS BEING TOO DEAR HERE!
OH, THANK YOU!

EVERY DOG HAS HIS DAY!

THE HOBBIES OF HOLLY

HOLLY JOHNSON is forever taking up some new hobby, to the dismay of her long-suffering friends, Audrey Poole and Jean Jackson. One evening Audrey and Jean call on Holly and, in her garden . . .

Jean handed up the torch.
AH!
TH-THERE'S SOMEONE UP HERE! I'M C-COMING DOWN! T-TWO HUGH EYES! YOU CAN DO YOUR OWN DONKEY WORK, HOLLY!
AUDREY! WHAT'S WRONG?
Audrey climbed down and Holly took her place.
SHE—SHE WASN'T JOKING!
COME OUT OF THERE, WHO-EVER YOU ARE! WHAT ARE YOU DOING IN MY GARDEN?
Suddenly—
OW! AN OWL!

Holly made a grab at a branch.
HELP!
REALLY, HOLLY! IMAGINE BEING FRIGHTENED OF AN OWL! YOU'RE REALLY BIRD-BRAINED!
HUH! YOU WEREN'T SO BRAVE YOURSELF, AUDREY!
WELL, WE'RE GOING HOME. I HOPE THIS IS THE END OF YOUR MOTH-HUNTING, HOLLY.
On the way home...
WE MUST STOP THIS HOBBY! COME ALONG TO MY HOUSE FOR COFFEE, JEAN, AND WE'LL TRY TO THINK UP SOME SCHEME.
Next morning, Holly glanced out of the window.
WOW! WHAT A SPECIMEN!

Holly leapt to her feet.
HOLLY!
Holly raced into the garden.
TOO LATE! IT'S GONE!
But the moth whisked away.
NO! THERE IT IS!
MISSED! WOW!

SHE FELL FOR AN IMITATION MOTH! IF WE CAN KEEP THIS UP A BIT LONGER, SHE'LL SOON BE FED-UP WITH MOTHS!
WHAT A ROTTEN TRICK! BUT I DON'T CARE! NOTHING WILL MAKE ME LOSE MY INTEREST IN MOTHS. IN FACT, I'M JUST GOING TO CHANGE INTO MY BEST DRESS TO ATTEND A LECTURE ABOUT MOTHS!
I BOUGHT THE DRESS AGES AGO BUT I HAVEN'T WORN IT YET. IT'LL CHEER ME UP.
WE MIGHT AS WELL WAIT UNTIL YOU CHANGE.
The girls waited while she changed.
LOOK AT MY DRESS—ALL HOLES! MOTHS HAVE GOT AT IT! IF ANYONE EVER MENTIONS MOTHS TO ME AGAIN....!
HARD LUCK, HOLLY—BUT AT LEAST IT'S CURED YOU OF THAT HOBBY!

THE LEGEND of BABA YAGA
ON the edge of a vast Russian forest, Nina lived with her stepmother while her father was away at war. Jealous of Nina's kind heart and popularity, the cruel stepmother kept her locked in a shed. Even there, she found a friend.
I ONLY HAVE A LITTLE BREAD, MOUSIKIN, BUT YOU ARE WELCOME TO SHARE IT.
Nina's stepmother opened the shed one day.
TAKE THIS NOTE TO YOUR AUNT BABA YAGA.
BABA YAGA, THE BONY-LEGGED WITCH? PLEASE DO NOT MAKE ME GO THERE!
But Nina's stepmother insisted.
I DON'T KNOW HOW TO GET TO BABA YAGA'S HUT IN THE FOREST.
FOLLOW YOUR NOSE, IDLE ONE! I HAVE GIVEN YOU FOOD TO EAT ON THE WAY.
In the heart of the forest . . .
POOR TREE! I SHALL MAKE YOU STRAIGHT AGAIN.
Nina felt hungry after the hard work of straightening the tree, but when she opened her food bundle . . .
A BONE! NEVER MIND. PERHAPS BABA YAGA WILL GIVE ME SOME BREAD.

At last, Nina reached Baba Yaga's hut.
POOR DOG, HOW HUNGRY YOU LOOK. TAKE MY BONE.
Nearby, a dwarf was chopping logs for Baba Yaga.
POOR LITTLE MAN! HOW HOT YOU LOOK. TAKE MY KERCHIEF TO WIPE YOUR BROW.
The witch's cat hissed.
DON'T LOOK SO CROSS, PUSS. THIS RIBBON WILL MAKE YOU LOOK PRETTY.
Trembling, Nina knocked on the door of the hut.
BABA YAGA, ARE YOU IN?
COME IN, MY PRETTY. I AM WAITING FOR YOU.
GOOD DAY, BABA YAGA. MY STEPMOTHER SENT YOU THIS NOTE.
WEAVE FOR ME, MY PRETTY, AND I WILL GO AND PREPARE A MEAL.

Every few minutes, Baba Yaga came to the door.
ARE YOU WEAVING, MY PRETTY?
I AM WEAVING, BABA YAGA.
When the witch was away, the dwarf crept in.
YOU WERE KIND TO ME, SO I WARN YOU THAT BABA YAGA MEANS TO EAT YOU WITH HER IRON TEETH!
OH! HOW CAN I ESCAPE? BABA YAGA WILL HEAR THAT THE LOOM HAS STOPPED!
GO QUICKLY! I SHALL TAKE YOUR PLACE AT THE LOOM.
But when the witch next called out to find out if Nina was still weaving and the dwarf answered, "I am weaving, Baba Yaga," she recognised his voice, and rushed in.
BETRAYED!! THE GIRL HAS ESCAPED!
AFTER HER!
NO! THE LITTLE GIRL WAS KIND TO US! WE WILL NOT HELP YOU!

The witch mounted her broomstick and flew after Nina.
STOP!
The tree that had been straightened remembered Nina's kindness and reached up its branches to grab Baba Yaga.
FOILED!
When Nina finally reached home, she found her father home from the wars. Her cruel stepmother had run away and was never seen again!
I'M SO GLAD YOU ARE HOME, FATHER.
I WON'T BE GOING AWAY AGAIN, I PROMISE YOU.

EMERGENCY EMMA

AT the large department store of Sharpes and Welbourne, Emma Dodds is the youngest member of the Emergency Team, trained to take over any job in any department as the need arises.

One morning, in the managing director's office, department heads and floor managers are having a final rehearsal for the reception of the Sheik of Shasbah, the richest man in the world.

On the ground floor, a few minutes later . . .

Meanwhile, on the first floor . . .

electrical
I HAVE COME TO DO MY CHRISTMAS SHOPPING.
IT'S ONLY MARCH!
WE CAN SHOP TOGETHER. VERY JOLLY FOR US ALL, YES?
NO, NO, MUCH LONGER, PLEASE. IT IS TO WIND ROUND THE NECK OF MY FAVOURITE CAMEL WHEN I LEAD HIM IN PROCESSION!
EMMA, TAKE THEIR HIGHNESSES FOR COFFEE WHILE WE SEARCH FOR OUR LONGEST SCARF.
YES, MR SHARPES.
HONESTLY, UNCLE JAMES! THE BET WAS THAT I WAS TO PASS MYSELF OFF AS A SHEIK AT SUE'S STORE, AND IF I GOT OUT UNDETECTED YOU'D GIVE ME FIFTY POUNDS FOR THE RAG FUND. YOU DIDN'T SAY YOU WOULD COME, TOO!
WELL, I KNOW, BUT I COULDN'T RESIST HAVING SOME FUN!
SO NEITHER OF THEM IS THE SHEIK OF SHASBAH! IT'S SUE'S BROTHER, TIM, AND THEIR CRAZY UNCLE JAMES! OH, WHY DID THEY HAVE TO CHOOSE TODAY? I'LL HAVE TO GET RID OF THEM BEFORE THE REAL SHEIK TURNS UP!
So, five minutes later . . .
THERE'S AN URGENT MESSAGE FOR YOUR HIGHNESSES! SERIOUS POLITICAL SITUATION! YOU ARE TO REPORT TO YOUR EMBASSY AT ONCE!
DEAR, DEAR! HOW DREADFUL! WE MUSTN'T DETAIN YOU. I'LL SEE YOU OUT MYSELF.

THEY WERE SO TAKEN IN, THEY EVEN GAVE US AN EMBASSY MESSAGE! I SAY, HOPE THE RIGHT CHAPS GET THE MESSAGE EVENTUALLY!
OH, YES, MY BOY, YOU WIN YOUR FIFTY POUNDS ALL RIGHT! BUT WHAT A SHAME OUR FUN WAS CUT SHORT! I COULD HAVE KEPT GOING ALL DAY! TAXI!
Meanwhile, back in Mr Sharpes' office...
I'VE JUST HAD THE EMBASSY ON THE 'PHONE AGAIN. THE SHEIK OF SHASBAH IS ON HIS WAY.
WHAT? YOU MEAN WE HAVEN'T HAD THE SHEIK OF SHASBAH? I CAN'T FACE ANOTHER SHEIK TODAY! WHAT ABOUT THE POLITICAL SITUATION?
WELL—ER—THAT'S IN A DIFFERENT PART OF THE MIDDLE EAST. NOW, SHALL I ROUND UP THE DEPARTMENT HEADS FOR YOU?
OH, VERY WELL. THEN YOU MAY GO FOR YOUR COFFEE BREAK.
On their way down to the canteen, Emma told Sue the whole story.
HONESTLY THOUGH, SUE, FANCY THEM HAVING THE NERVE TO CHOOSE THE VERY STORE WHERE YOU WORK!
THAT'S THEM ALL OVER— THE RISKIER THE BETTER! BUT, EMMA, WHY DIDN'T YOU GET RID OF THEM JUST BY TELLING THEM YOU KNEW WHO THEY WERE?
THAT'S OBVIOUS! I WANTED TIM TO GET HIS FIFTY POUNDS FOR THE FUND!

This enormous polar bear at the zoo didn't mind me photographing him, although he seems to be saying, "Hurry up! I can't sit here all day!"

Norma Pearson,
Norwich.

This 'plane has just landed on the beach at the Isle of Barra, in the Outer Hebrides. The flying times depend on the tide—the 'planes can only land when the tide is out.

Susan Duncan, Bristol.

In the summer I photographed this rose in the garden. There were dozens then, and the garden was a riot of colour.

Anne Clark,
Bath.

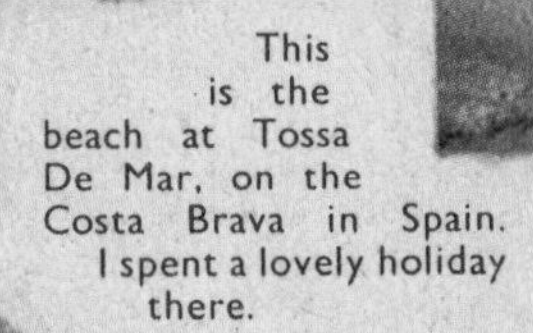

This is the beach at Tossa De Mar, on the Costa Brava in Spain. I spent a lovely holiday there.

Karen
Pettigrew,
Liverpool.

These penguins aren't really giving each other the cold shoulder —it just looks that way!

Betty Tennant,
Saltcoats.

This mother sheep and her lamb mad friends with my b sister, June, and enjoy the sugar lumps s gave them.

Barbara Laing,
Cornwall.